Science

3-4

Written by
Marilyn Marks

Editor: Carla Hamaguchi
Illustrator: Jane Yamada
Designer/Production: Moonhee Pak/Terri Lamadrid
Cover Designer: Barbara Peterson
Art Director: Tom Cochrane
Project Director: Carolea Williams

D1399850

Table of Contents

Introduction

Each book in the *Power Practice*™ series contains over 100 ready-to-use activity pages to provide students with skill practice. The fun activities can be used to supplement and enhance what you are teaching in your classroom. Give an activity page to students as independent class work, or send the pages home as homework to reinforce skills taught in class. An answer key is provided for quick reference.

The practical and creative activities in the science series provide the perfect way to help students develop the science process skills of observing, sorting, classifying, comparing, and analyzing.

Science 3–4 provides activities that illustrate and explain concepts in life science, earth science, and physical science, and the topics covered correlate with current science standards. Use the reproducible activity pages to enrich students' study of these key topics:
• Biomes and Ecosystems
• Animals and Adaptations
• Oceanography
• Plants and Adaptations
• Natural Resources
• Geology
• Astronomy
• Electricity and Magnetism
• Light Energy
• Heat Energy
• Chemistry

Use these ready-to-go activities to "recharge" skill review and give students the power to succeed!

Name _____ Date _____

What Is a Biome?

BIOMES AND ECOSYSTEMS

The word **biome** describes a large land area with a particular climate and vegetation. Each biome can be identified by its temperature and the amount of rainfall it receives. Desert biomes are hot and very dry. Grassland or prairie biomes are mild and dry. Hardwood and evergreen forests are cool and moist. Tropical rain forests are described as hot and very wet. The arctic tundra is very cold and dry.

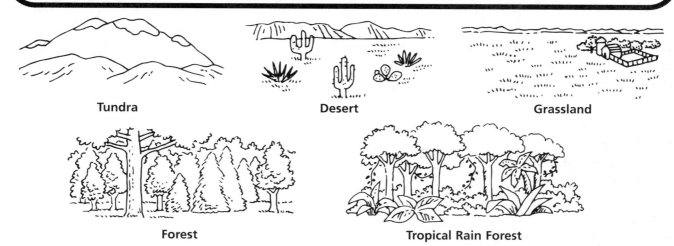

Tundra   **Desert**   **Grassland**

Forest   **Tropical Rain Forest**

Use the words in the box to complete the sentences. You can use a word more than once.

desert	grassland	forest	tundra	rain forest

1 Snow covers the frozen ground in the _____ for most of the year.

2 You would find cows, sheep, and horses living in a _____.

3 A jungle is also called a tropical _____.

4 Cactus plants would live in a _____.

5 A _____ is a biome that has lots of trees growing in it.

6 The climate in a _____ is mild and dry.

7 A _____ is the biome that gets the most rain.

8 A _____ biome is hot and has very little rain most of the year.

Name _____ Date _____

What Is a Food Chain?

BIOMES AND ECOSYSTEMS

Green plants use the sun, air, and water to make food. Animals called **herbivores** eat the plants. Some animals eat other animals. They are called **carnivores**. Other animals, called **omnivores**, eat plants and animals. When plants and animals die, small organisms called **decomposers** cause their remains to decay. This process of who is eating whom is called a **food chain**.

Look at the picture. Follow the directions to mark the picture and answer the questions.

1 Color the food makers (producers) green.

2 Circle the herbivore.

3 Draw an **X** on the carnivore.

4 Where are most decomposers found? Circle one: air   water   soil

Science • 3–4 © 2005 Creative Teaching Press

Name _____ Date _____

Food Chain Crossword Puzzle

BIOMES AND ECOSYSTEMS

Complete the crossword puzzle. Use the words from the box for help.

decomposer	carnivore	environment	consumer	omnivore	prey
producer	herbivore	air	sun	earth	

Across

1. A green plant that makes the food
4. What all animals need to breathe
8. The planet we live on
9. An animal that eats plants and meat
10. An animal that eats plants

Down

1. An animal that is hunted for food
2. Second step in a food chain; the role of animals
3. Source of energy for the food chain
5. All of our surroundings
6. An animal that eats other animals
7. Part of the food chain that causes dead plants and animals to decay

Science • 3–4 © 2005 Creative Teaching Press

Name _____ Date _____

Food Webs

Biomes and Ecosystems

The sun, water, soil, and air are nonliving parts of an ecosystem. All the plants and animals are the living parts. Within any ecosystem there will be several different food chains. Many of these food chains overlap and interact. We call these overlapping food chains **food webs**. Parts of the food web depend on other parts.

Look at the picture. Follow the directions to mark the picture and answer the questions.

1 Draw a line from the sun to two producers.

2 Name 3 animals that eat the plants: _____, _____, _____.

3 Put a ✓ by all the things that need water.

4 The chickens and cows depend on the _____ to take care of them. In return, they provide food for him to eat.

5 Circle the animal that can give the farmer food and wool.

Science • 3–4 © 2005 Creative Teaching Press

Name _____ Date _____

Deserts

BIOMES AND ECOSYSTEMS

A **desert** is a hot, dry biome that receives 10 inches (25.4 cm) or less of rainfall a year. Plants and animals that live in a desert have to be adapted to living with very little water. Cactus plants store water in their stems. Their leaves are small spines. Some desert animals sleep during the day and come out at night when it is cooler.

Look at the pictures and complete the descriptions.

1 I am a very tall cactus that can store water inside my stem. I am a

_____.

2 I have big ears, which give off heat to cool me off as I hop very fast. I am a

_____.

3 I like to run instead of fly. I eat lizards and snakes. I am a

_____.

4 I hunt at night and howl to call my friends. I am a

_____.

5 I am a small cactus that makes a fruit that looks like a pear. I am a

_____.

6 I get my name because I can jump very high. I can go a long time without drinking water. I am a

_____.

Tropical Rain Forests

Biomes and Ecosystems

Most tropical **rain forests** are found near the equator. These forests are hot all year long and receive at least 90 inches (229 cm) of rain a year. A tropical rain forest grows in layers. The tallest trees stick out above the **canopy**. The **understory** is home to smaller trees. The **forest floor** is shady. There are more kinds of plants and animals in a tropical rain forest than in any other biome.

Read each statement. Write **T** if the statement is true or **F** if it is false.

1 _____ Many birds live in the canopy layer.

2 _____ The forest floor is very sunny.

3 _____ Tropical rain forests are always hot and humid.

4 _____ Tropical rain forests are always green.

5 _____ Vines and orchid plants grow on tropical tree branches.

6 _____ Some animals live in the trees and never descend to the ground.

7 _____ We can eat a lot of the fruits that grow in a tropical rain forest.

8 _____ Tropical rain forests are the wettest biome.

9 _____ Most tropical rain forests are found in the far northern parts of the earth.

10 _____ Many animals we see in a zoo really come from a tropical rain forest.

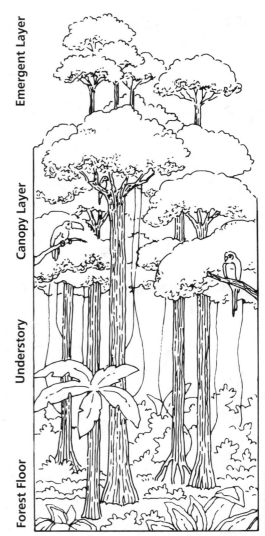

Emergent Layer

Canopy Layer

Understory

Forest Floor

Name _____ Date _____

Evergreen Forests

BIOMES AND ECOSYSTEMS

Evergreen forests grow where the climate is cool and moist. They receive around 35–75 inches (89–191 cm) of rain or snow a year. It snows a lot in the wintertime. Trees in an evergreen forest have thin, needle-like, or scale-like leaves. These trees make cones that carry their seeds. Many evergreen forests are found in mountainous regions.

Write the letter of the correct answer.

1 _____ Which of these is **NOT** an evergreen forest tree?
- **a.** pine
- **b.** oak
- **c.** fir
- **d.** spruce

2 _____ Trees in an evergreen forest produce _____.
- **a.** flowers
- **b.** cones
- **c.** fruits
- **d.** vegetables

3 _____ It snows a lot in an evergreen forest during the ____.
- **a.** fall
- **b.** summer
- **c.** winter
- **d.** spring

4 _____ Trees in an evergreen forest have leaves that are ____.
- **a.** needle-like
- **b.** broad and flat
- **c.** round
- **d.** wide

5 _____ Evergreen forests are found _____.
- **a.** where it's cool and moist
- **b.** in dry places
- **c.** near the poles
- **d.** in the savanna

6 _____ Which animals live in an evergreen forest?
- **a.** bears and squirrels
- **b.** monkeys and tigers
- **c.** camels and scorpions
- **d.** polar bears and reindeer

7 _____ We use the wood from evergreen trees for _____.
- **a.** building homes
- **b.** making cardboard
- **c.** making paper
- **d.** all of the above

Name _____ Date _____

Hardwood Forests

Biomes and Ecosystems

Trees in a **hardwood forest** have broad, flat leaves. Many of these trees change color in the fall and lose their leaves in the winter. They are also called **deciduous trees**. All hardwood trees produce flowers. Some of them package their seeds in a fruit or nut. We find hardwood forests in places that are cool and moist. They receive 35–70 inches (89–178 cm) of rain a year.

Read each statement. Write **T** if the statement is true or **F** if it is false.

1 _____ Hardwood forests are found farther north than the evergreen forests.

2 _____ Many hardwood, or deciduous, trees lose their leaves in the winter.

3 _____ Hardwood trees have broad, flat leaves.

4 _____ Hardwood trees have trunks that are easier to climb.

5 _____ Hardwood trees make seeds inside of cones.

6 _____ Hardwood forests get more of their moisture as rain and much less as snow.

7 _____ Hardwood trees produce flowers.

8 _____ Birch, ash, oak, and elm are examples of hardwood trees.

9 _____ We make furniture from the wood of many hardwood trees.

10 _____ Banana, mango, and papaya are fruits made by hardwood trees.

Science • 3–4 © 2005 Creative Teaching Press

Name _____ Date _____

Grasslands and Prairies

BIOMES AND ECOSYSTEMS

A **prairie** is a type of grassland that does not get enough rain for trees to grow. We often find prairies between forests and deserts. **Grassland** areas that get a little more rainfall will have scattered trees. The African savanna and Australian outback are examples of this type of grassland. All grasslands have a warm, mild, and dry climate. Many grassland areas have been made into farms and ranches.

Use the words in the box to complete the sentences.

| warm | Africa | food | giraffes | lions | cows | horses | kangaroo | grassland |

1 The climate in a grassland is usually _____.

2 Two animals that live in the African savanna are _____

and _____.

3 Many grassland areas are used as farms to grow _____.

4 Two animals we could find in North American grasslands are

_____ and _____.

5 The _____ lives in Australia's grasslands.

6 A continent that has a large savanna is _____.

7 Corn, oats, wheat, and cotton all grow in a _____.

Science • 3–4 © 2005 Creative Teaching Press

Name _____ Date _____

Arctic Tundra

BIOMES AND ECOSYSTEMS

The **tundra** biome is located in the far northern parts of the earth. The tundra is very cold and dry. It is so cold that the ground stays frozen most of the year. Only about 6 inches (15 cm) of the ground thaws out during the short summer. Arctic plants grow close to the ground to avoid the wind. Some arctic animals hibernate, while others migrate farther south during the harsh winter.

Put a ✓ by each statement that describes the tundra.

1 _____ There is very little sunlight during the winter.

2 _____ The tundra is found near the equator.

3 _____ It rains often in the tundra.

4 _____ The ground stays frozen most of the year.

5 _____ Lemmings, polar bears, musk oxen, and caribou (reindeer) live in the tundra.

6 _____ Some arctic animals migrate farther south during the winter.

7 _____ Summer lasts a long time in the tundra.

8 _____ Penguins live in the tundra.

9 _____ The plants are small and grow close to the ground.

10 _____ Arctic plants have to grow quickly when conditions are right.

Science • 3–4 © 2005 Creative Teaching Press

Name _____ Date _____

Life in a Marsh

BIOMES AND ECOSYSTEMS

A **marsh** is a wetland ecosystem. There are freshwater marshes and saltwater marshes. Freshwater marshes are found along rivers and lakes or in low-lying inland regions. Saltwater marshes are found along ocean coasts. Marshes are wetland areas where no trees grow. Many reeds and grasses are growing there, even in the water. Marshes are home to many migratory birds and fish.

Use the words in the box to complete the sentences.

floods	pollution	birds	food	recreation	destroyed	wetland	grasses

1 As water flows through a marsh, the plants help to remove

_____.

2 A marsh is a _____ ecosystem, which means part of the ground is under water.

3 Marsh wetlands help to prevent _____ by holding extra water.

4 Marshes are home to many migratory _____.

5 Marshes are also places for _____, such as boating and fishing.

6 Marsh animals such as fish and clams provide us with _____.

7 Unfortunately, many marsh wetlands have been _____ to make way for farms and cities.

8 Marshes are wetlands without trees, but lots of _____ grow there.

Name _____ Date _____

Life in a Swamp

BIOMES AND ECOSYSTEMS

A **swamp** is a wetland ecosystem where trees and shrubs grow in the water. There are freshwater swamps and saltwater swamps. Saltwater, or mangrove, swamps are found along tropical ocean coasts in warmer regions. Freshwater swamps are found in low-lying regions or near rivers. Alligators and crayfish live in a freshwater swamp.

Match each item to its description.

1 _____ freshwater swamp trees

2 _____ freshwater swamp animals

3 _____ saltwater swamp trees

4 _____ saltwater swamp animals

5 _____ found along tropical ocean coasts

6 _____ found in low regions or near rivers

A. crayfish, alligator, turtle, frog

B. water oak, bald cypress, willow

C. sea horse, mangrove tree crab, oyster

D. mangroves

E. freshwater swamp

F. saltwater swamp

Name _____ Date _____

Life in a Bog

BIOMES AND ECOSYSTEMS

A **bog** is an unusual ecosystem found in colder regions. It is sort of like a pond with moss growing all over the surface. Sometimes you cannot even see there is water hidden underneath. The dead moss plants slowly fill up the bog so the land becomes spongy. Cranberries and a spice called rosemary grow in some bogs.

Use the words in the box to complete the sentences.

| moss | water | cranberries | rosemary | colder | ecosystem |

1 _____ plants grow all over the surface of a bog.

2 Bogs only form in places that have _____ weather.

3 The land in a bog can feel shaky or spongy because there is

_____ underneath.

4 The _____ that people in the U.S. eat at Thanksgiving grow in a bog.

5 A spice called _____ can grow in a bog, too.

6 A bog is an unusual wetland _____.

Name _____ Date _____

Animal Migration

ANIMALS AND ADAPTATIONS

Migration means moving from one place to another. Many birds, whales, fish, caribou, and even some insects migrate during certain times of the year. Some seek better climates. Others migrate in search of more food. Some migrate during mating and breeding season. Then the animals, or their offspring, return to the area where they started.

Number the sentences in order to show how the animal migrates. The first step has been done for you.

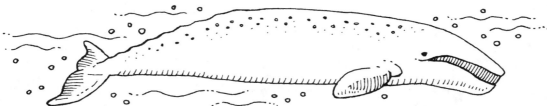

_____ In early December the gray whales begin migrating south to Baja California, Mexico.

__1__ Babies are born off the coast of Baja California, Mexico.

_____ Gray whales spend the summer and fall feeding in the ocean around Alaska.

_____ From April to June the babies and mothers swim north to Alaska.

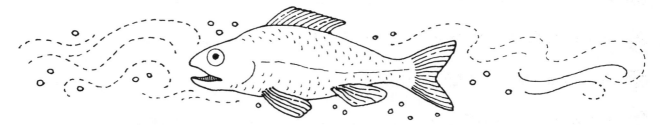

__1__ Pacific salmon lay eggs in a stream. The parents die after the eggs are laid.

_____ Young fish swim downstream towards the mouth of the river.

_____ Salmon swim out to deep water in the ocean and live there for 2–4 years.

_____ Eggs hatch into babies called "fry," which live in the river until they are bigger.

_____ Salmon leave the ocean and swim up the river to the place of their birth.

Science • 3–4 © 2005 Creative Teaching Press

How Animals Protect Themselves

ANIMALS AND ADAPTATIONS

Some animals have claws, horns, or hooves. Others have sharp teeth or beaks. There are animals that disguise themselves to look like their surroundings, while others warn off enemies with bright colors. Angry sounds can scare away an enemy, too. Animals protect themselves in many ways.

Use the words in the box to complete the sentences.

fangs and a hiss	sharp teeth	claws	tentacles	horns
bad smell	bright colors	bark	roar	quills

1 A porcupine protects itself with _____.

2 A skunk produces a _____.

3 A butterfly warns its enemies with its _____.

4 A dog scares its enemies with its _____.

5 A lion uses its loud _____.

6 A lobster protects itself with _____.

7 A snake protects itself with _____.

8 A buffalo has _____.

9 A jellyfish protects itself with _____.

10 A shark has _____.

Name _____ Date _____

Bird Beaks and Feet

ANIMALS AND ADAPTATIONS

Birds' beaks and feet are shaped to help them adapt to their environment. Water birds have webbed feet for swimming. Other birds have separate toes for walking or curved claws for perching. Beaks come in all shapes and sizes. Each type helps the bird catch its food.

Identify how each type of bird feet and beak are used.

walking	swimming	perching	scratching

❶ _____

❷ _____

❸ _____

❹ _____

straining water	fishing	eating insects	sucking nectar

❶ _____

❷ _____

❸ _____

❹ _____

Science • 3–4 © 2005 Creative Teaching Press

Name _____ Date _____

How Animals Find and Catch Food

ANIMALS AND ADAPTATIONS

Animals have many adaptations for finding or catching food. They may have sticky tongues, sharp teeth, beaks, claws, tentacles, or a keen sense of smell. Dolphins and bats use a type of sonar called **echolocation** to find their food. Many spiders spin a sticky web to trap their dinner.

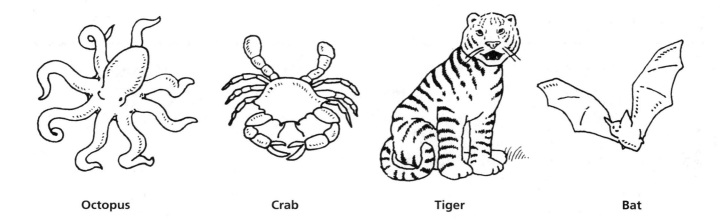

| Octopus | Crab | Tiger | Bat |

Use the words in the box to complete the sentences.

| smell | tentacles | claws | sticky tongue | sharp teeth | echolocation | web |

1 An octopus uses its _____ to catch its food.

2 A crab uses its _____ to catch food.

3 A frog has a _____ that it flicks out to catch insects.

4 A pig uses its nose and keen sense of _____ to find its food.

5 A tiger has _____ in its mouth to help it catch food.

6 A dolphin uses bouncing sound waves, a method called

_____, to find food.

7 Many spiders spin a sticky _____ to catch their food.

Science • 3-4 © 2005 Creative Teaching Press

Name _____ Date _____

Animals Adapt to Their Environment

ANIMALS AND ADAPTATIONS

The ability of animals to adjust to their surroundings is called **adaptation**. Animals need to adapt to the various conditions of the environment where they live. They may live where it is windy, cold, hot, or dry. The ground might be rocky, muddy, or slippery. The animal will die if it cannot adapt successfully. That is why we find different types of animals living in different environments.

Follow the directions to label each statement.

- Write **C** if the adaptation protects the animal from the cold.
- Write **H** if the adaptation protects the animal from the heat.
- Write **W** if the adaptation helps the animal adapt to a lack of water.
- Write **G** if the adaptation helps the animal walk or climb over the ground.
- Write **F** if the adaptation helps the animal survive where food is scarce.

1 _____ Many polar animals have thick layers of fat under their skin.

2 _____ Mountain goats have flexible, rubbery hooves on their feet.

3 _____ Beavers store food underwater near their lodge before winter comes.

4 _____ The kangaroo rat can survive with very little water by eating cactus seeds.

5 _____ Camels store fat in their hump.

6 _____ Many mountain animals are covered with thick fur.

7 _____ Some animals of the desert hide under a bush or in a burrow during the day.

8 _____ Polar bears have flat feet with pads of fur growing on the soles.

9 _____ Many lizards rest on rocks in the early morning sunshine.

10 _____ Many animals shed hair or fur when spring comes.

Science • 3–4 © 2005 Creative Teaching Press

How Animals Reproduce

ANIMALS AND ADAPTATIONS

Most **invertebrate animals**, like insects and worms, lay small eggs. **Vertebrate animals** such as fish, reptiles, birds, and amphibians lay eggs, too. A few fish and most mammals give birth to live young. Many animal parents do not care for their babies. Those animals usually lay lots of eggs because many of the babies will not survive on their own. Animal parents that take care of their young usually have fewer babies at a time.

 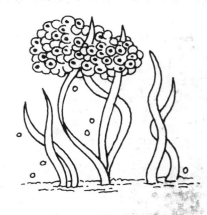

Follow the directions to label how each animal reproduces.

- Write **eggs** or **born alive** to tell how the animal reproduces.
- Circle the names of 4 animals that do not take care of their babies.
- Draw a box around the names of 4 animals that take care of their babies after they **are** hatched or born.

1 Chicken _____

2 Frog _____

3 Dog _____

4 Insects _____

5 Human beings _____

6 Most fish _____

7 Alligator _____

8 Worms _____

Name _____ Date _____

Spider or Insect?

ANIMALS AND ADAPTATIONS

You can tell the difference between a spider and an insect if you look carefully. Spiders and insects do not have the same number of legs. Their bodies are not divided into the same number of parts. Their eyes are different, too. And most insects have wings and antennae. Most spiders spin silk. And spiders like to eat insects.

Spider

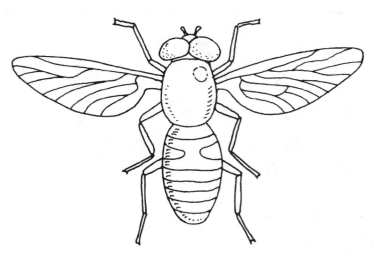

Insect

List 5 different characteristics of spiders and insects.

Spider Characteristics

1 Legs: _____

2 Eyes: _____

_____

3 Body parts: _____

_____

4 _____

5 _____

Insect Characteristics

1 Legs: _____

2 Eyes: _____

_____

3 Body parts: _____

_____

4 _____

5 _____

Name _____ Date _____

Butterfly or Moth?

ANIMALS AND ADAPTATIONS

Butterflies and moths are both insects, but they are not the same. Butterflies are mainly active during the daytime, whereas moths prefer to fly in the late afternoon and evening. Butterflies and moths do not eat the same things. And butterflies are quiet, but many moths can make sounds.

Look at the characteristics of butterflies and moths. Follow the directions to mark the pictures.

| Butterfly | thin body | slender antennae | wings up when it rests | caterpillar makes a chrysalis |
| Moth | plump body | feather-like antennae | wings flat when it rests | caterpillar makes a cocoon |

1 Color all of the butterflies orange.

2 Color all of the moths brown.

3 Draw an **X** on the insects that are not butterflies or moths.

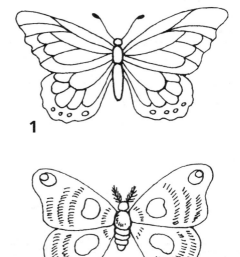

1

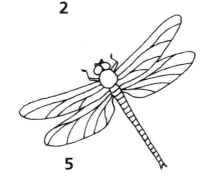

2

3

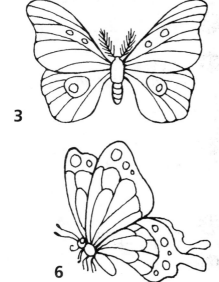

4

5

6

Name _____ Date _____

What Animal Are You Like?

Sometimes we use animal expressions to describe the way people are behaving. For example, have you ever heard anyone say, *He sure is crabby today*? Perhaps you have heard the expression, *She's as peaceful as a dove*. There are many characteristics that we identify with certain animals. When people act that way, we often use an animal expression to describe them.

Draw a line from the person's description to the matching animal picture.

1 A graceful person

 Peacock

2 A clumsy person

 Swan

3 A very busy person

 Bat

4 A sly person

 Owl

5 A person who can't see well

 Bee

6 A wise person

 Goose

7 A proud person

 Ox

8 A silly person

 Fox

Name _____ Date _____

Animals of Long Ago

ANIMALS AND ADAPTATIONS

The first small mammals appeared on the earth near the end of the time when dinosaurs lived. Thousands of years later, large mammals like the mastodon, giant sloth, woolly mammoth, and saber-toothed cats appeared. All of these ancient mammals are now extinct. Most of them died out during the last Ice Age, when huge glaciers covered large parts of the earth. Scientists have found fossils that help us learn what these animals were like.

Mastodon   **Woolly Mammoth**   **Saber-toothed Cat**

Read each statement. Write **T** if the statement is true or **F** if it is false.

1 _____ The woolly mammoth and saber-toothed cats roamed the earth with the dinosaurs.

2 _____ The woolly mammoth was the largest of four ancient, elephant-like animals.

3 _____ The mastodon and woolly mammoth are now extinct.

4 _____ Mastodons had tusks that curled upward in a half-circle.

5 _____ Fossils of saber-toothed cats and woolly mammoths have been found in North America.

6 _____ There were humans on the earth before the woolly mammoths died out.

7 _____ Saber-toothed cats had two large, pointed canine teeth in the front of their mouth.

8 _____ Saber-toothed cats were powerful hunters.

Name _____   Date _____

Tide Pools

OCEANOGRAPHY

Tide pools are shallow, rocky shore areas that are exposed to the air when the tide is out. When the tide is in, called **high tide**, most of the plants and animals are covered with water. As the tide goes out, many of the animals have to move into one of the pools of water that collect between the rocks. Or, they move into the deeper water at the edge of the ocean. Some of the animals can survive while the tide is out. They cling to rocks and keep water inside their shell.

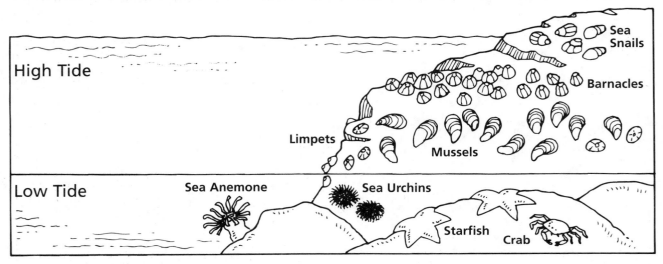

Look at the picture and answer the questions.

1 Four animals that can survive out of the water during low tide are

_____,   _____ ,

_____, and _____.

2 Four animals that have to always be in the water during low tide are the

_____,   _____ ,

_____, and _____.

3 What do you think happens to the seaweed plants when the tide goes out?

_____

Science • 3–4 © 2005 Creative Teaching Press

Name _____ Date _____

Sandy Beaches

OCEANOGRAPHY

Sandy beaches are very different from rocky shores. The sandy beach area is home to many seashell animals and lugworms, which bury themselves in the sand. Other animals, like fiddler crabs and beach fleas, crawl over the sand looking for something to eat. Some sandy beach areas have scattered clumps of grass or seaweed. Others are just bare sand. The ocean waves constantly wash up on the shore, bringing nutrients to the animals hidden in the sand.

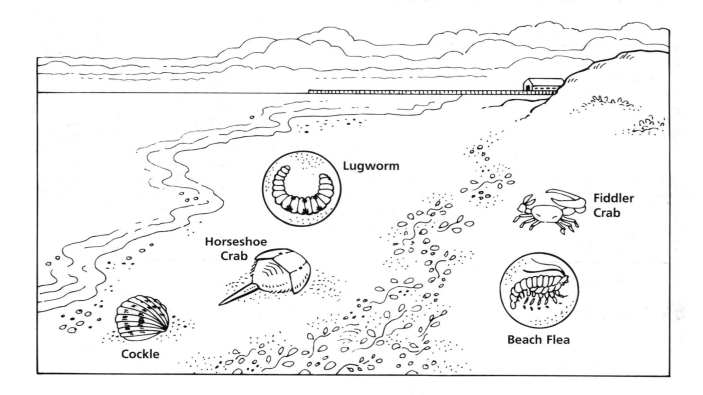

Put a ✓ by all the animals that live on a sandy beach. Some may be buried in the sand.

❶ _____ Sea anemone

❷ _____ Sand dollar

❸ _____ Sea urchin

❹ _____ Beach flea

❺ _____ Lugworm

❻ _____ Limpet

❼ _____ Fiddler crab

❽ _____ Cockle

❾ _____ Sea star

❿ _____ Horseshoe crab

The Ocean's Sunlight Zone

OCEANOGRAPHY

The **sunlight zone** goes from the surface of the water down to about 300–400 feet (91–122 m). This is the area where the sunlight can penetrate through the water and the part of the ocean where plants can grow. About 90% of all ocean animals live in the sunlight zone. There is an abundance of food provided by all the seaweed and plankton organisms.

Match each description to the animal that lives in the sunlight zone.

1 _____ I am a large, fast fish that people like to eat.

2 _____ I have eight legs and am very shy.

3 _____ I am the largest mammal in the ocean.

4 _____ I am a small fish used for fishing bait and food for people.

5 _____ I float in the water and sting with my tentacles.

6 _____ I have very sharp teeth, and I have even bitten people.

7 _____ I look like a snake, but I am a fish.

8 _____ I am a friendly mammal that makes a squeaky sound.

9 _____ I am a bird, and I look for something to eat in the shallow water.

A. jellyfish

B. sea gull

C. herring

D. eel

E. blue shark

F. dolphin

G. tuna

H. blue whale

I. octopus

Name _____ Date _____

The Ocean's Twilight and Midnight Zones

OCEANOGRAPHY

As you go deeper in the ocean, the water gets colder and darker. The **twilight zone** extends from around 400 feet (122 m) down to 3,000 feet (914 m). The **midnight zone** includes everything below 3,000 feet. The pressure of the water also increases. No plants can live down this deep. Most animals that live here are small, strange-looking, and bioluminescent (they glow).

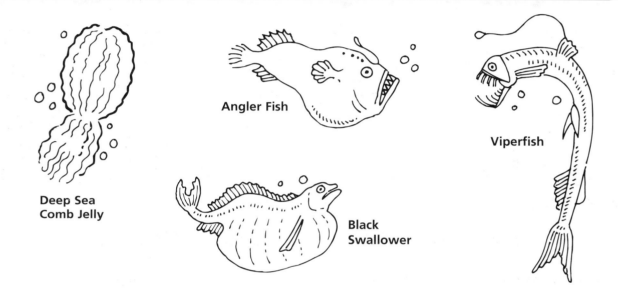

Deep Sea
Comb Jelly

Angler Fish

Viperfish

Black
Swallower

Read each statement. Write **T** if the statement is true or **F** if it is false.

1 _____ Many animals in the twilight and midnight zones are bioluminescent.

2 _____ You could swim down into the twilight zone.

3 _____ Near the ocean bottom the temperature of the water is freezing.

4 _____ Many large fish live in the midnight zone.

5 _____ It is hard to see in the twilight and midnight zones.

6 _____ Some animals glow to help them attract food.

7 _____ You need to be in a submarine or diving vessel to observe the midnight zone.

8 _____ We often eat fish that live in the midnight zone.

Name _____ Date _____

Life on a Coral Reef

OCEANOGRAPHY

Coral reefs are found in warm, clear, shallow tropical water. The corals use minerals in the ocean water to construct a rock-hard home around them. Thousands of coral animals live together and gradually build the reef. Coral reefs are some of the most beautiful and exotic places in the ocean. The Great Barrier Reef off the coast of Australia is the world's largest coral reef.

Use the words in the box to complete the sentences.

skinny	starfish	staghorn	fan	fat	sea urchin

1 A softer coral that sways back and forth in the water is called

_____ coral.

2 A pointy, branched coral that looks like antlers is called

_____ coral.

3 Many coral reef fish are _____ from side to side, which makes it easier to stop and start.

4 The Porcupine Puffer fish can swallow water and get big and

_____ to keep from being eaten.

5 Two spiny-skinned invertebrates that live on a coral reef are the

_____ and the _____.

Name _____ Date _____

Sea Turtles

OCEANOGRAPHY

There are several kinds of sea turtles. The largest is the Leatherback, weighing up to 660 pounds (290 kg). The smallest is Kemp's Ridley, which weighs about 90 pounds (41 kg). All sea turtles are reptiles and must surface to take air into their lungs. However, sea turtles can stay underwater for a long time. The females venture ashore every year to lay their eggs in the sand.

Put a ✓ by the sentences that describe the way sea turtles live.

1 _____ Sea turtles are able to breathe under the water.

2 _____ Sea turtles come in different sizes.

3 _____ Adult sea turtles spend most of their time in deeper water.

4 _____ All sea turtles are endangered.

5 _____ All sea turtles except the Leatherback have a hard shell.

6 _____ Sea turtles can pull their head and legs back into their shell.

7 _____ A sea turtle uses its legs like flippers for swimming.

8 _____ Females come ashore to lay their eggs in the sand.

9 _____ When sea turtle babies hatch, they must race to the sea before predators can grab them.

Name _____ Date _____

Marine Mammals

OCEANOGRAPHY

There are many types of marine mammals, from small sea otters to large whales. There are even two kinds of whales. Large whales are called **baleen whales**. Instead of teeth, they have rows and rows of bristles hanging from their top jaw—sort of like a toothbrush! Small whales, which include dolphins and porpoises, all have teeth. The **orca**, or killer whale, gets its name because it is the only whale that hunts and eats other marine mammals.

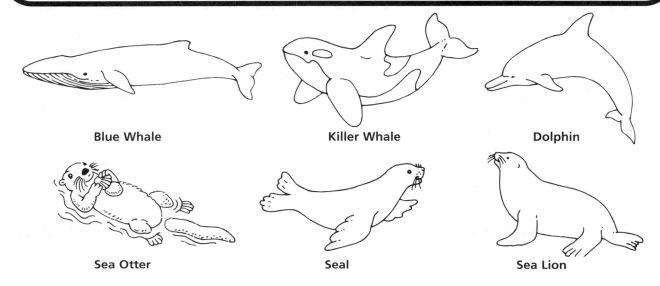

Blue Whale	**Killer Whale**	**Dolphin**
Sea Otter	**Seal**	**Sea Lion**

Use the words in the box to complete the sentences.

blubber	baleen	teeth	sea lion	walrus	sea otter

1 Most marine mammals have a thick layer of _____ under their skin that keeps them warm.

2 The smallest marine mammal is the _____, which lies on its back to eat shellfish.

3 Smaller whales are meat eaters and have _____ in their mouth.

4 The _____ is a marine mammal with large tusks.

5 The _____ is a marine mammal that can be trained to do tricks.

6 The largest whales have rows and rows of _____ in their mouth, which strain the water for krill and small fish to eat.

Name _____ Date _____

Types of Fish

OCEANOGRAPHY

> Most fish in the ocean have a skeleton made of hard bone. Sharks, rays, and skates are called **cartilaginous fish**. Their skeleton is mainly made of flexible cartilage (like your outer ears). The only hard bone they have is in their jaws. The skin of bony fish is covered with fairly smooth, wet, slippery scales. The skin of sharks and their relatives feels more like sandpaper.

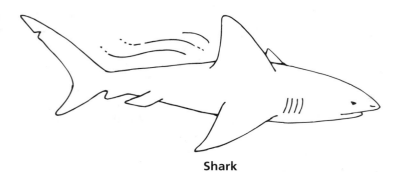

Shark

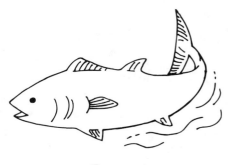

Tuna

Write **B** if the sentence describes bony fish, **C** if it describes cartilaginous fish, or **D** if it describes both kinds of fish.

1 _____ These fish breathe with gills.

2 _____ These fish are covered with smooth, wet, slippery scales.

3 _____ The skin of these fish feels rough, like sandpaper.

4 _____ You need to be careful of little bones when you eat this kind of fish.

5 _____ The skeleton of these fish is flexible and rubbery.

6 _____ Sharks, stingrays, and skates belong to this group of fish.

7 _____ Tuna, swordfish, and flounder belong to this group of fish.

8 _____ Most of these fish are good swimmers.

Science • 3–4 © 2005 Creative Teaching Press

Name _____ Date _____

Plankton

OCEANOGRAPHY

Did you know that there are millions of tiny plants and animals in the ocean that you cannot see? They are so small that you would need a microscope to see most of them. These plants and animals are called **plankton**. Most of them just float and drift along with the ocean currents. The tiny plant plankton gives the ocean water its color. Plankton is an important source of food for larger sea animals.

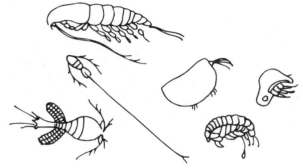

Animal Plankton

Plant Plankton

Use the words in the box to complete the sentences.

food	microscope	drift	plankton	plant	animal

1 Tiny floating plants and animals in the ocean water are called

_____.

2 To see most plankton organisms you would need a _____.

3 The tremendous number of _____ plankton gives the ocean water its color.

4 Most plankton organisms cannot swim; they just _____ along with the ocean currents.

5 Plankton is important because it is used for _____ by many larger sea animals.

6 A lot of the plant plankton is eaten by the _____ plankton organisms.

Science • 3–4 © 2005 Creative Teaching Press

Name _____ Date _____

Seashell Animals

OCEANOGRAPHY

Seashell animals are called **mollusks**. All sea snails, abalone, and limpets are called **univalves**. These mollusks have one shell that protects the animal inside. Clams, oysters, and scallops are called **bivalves**. They have two shells that fit together. Most seashell animals move very slowly using a muscular foot. However, the scallop is able to swim.

Oyster

Abalone

Scallop

Whelk

Limpet

Read each statement. Write **T** if the statement is true or **F** if it is false.

1 _____ Mollusks move around using a muscular foot.

2 _____ Seashell animals with one shell are called bivalves.

3 _____ The hard shell protects the soft body of a mollusk.

4 _____ The abalone is a bivalve.

5 _____ Oysters are mollusks that can swim around in the water.

6 _____ We often find seashells that have washed up on the beach.

7 _____ Limpets are classified as univalves.

Name _____ Date _____

Seabirds

OCEANOGRAPHY

Some seabirds, like the albatross, spend most of their life over the open ocean. Others live along the shores. One of the most common birds seen near the shore is the seagull. Cormorants, gannets, and petrels fly over the water and dive down underneath to catch fish. Pelicans dive for fish and catch them in their pouch. Other seabirds, like sandpipers and willets, wade in the shallow water and walk along the beach looking for tasty things to eat.

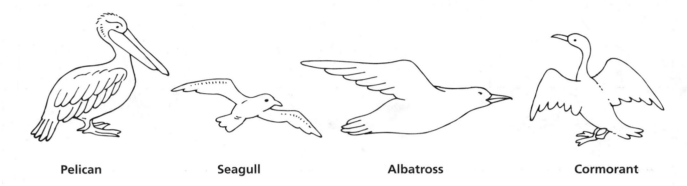

| Pelican | Seagull | Albatross | Cormorant |

Use the words in the box to complete the sentences.

| swim | dive | wade | albatross | seagull | pelican |

1 Many seabirds have webbed feet that help them _____ in the water.

2 Some seabirds _____ underwater from high in the air.

3 The large _____ spends most of its life away from shore, over the open ocean.

4 One of the most common seabirds often seen near the shore is the

_____.

5 Some seabirds walk along the shore and _____ in the shallow water.

6 The _____ has a pouch for holding the fish it catches.

Name _____ Date _____

Sea Life Puzzle

Cross out all the names of animals that live in the sea. Then use the first letters of the remaining words to spell out a message at the bottom of the page.

Tiger	Horse	Tuna	Earthworm	Seagull	Crab	Skunk
Eagle	Marlin	Antelope	Shrimp	Gorilla	Plankton	Inchworm
Salmon	Viper	Halibut	Elephant	Sloth	Dolphin	Underground Animals
Skunk	Sand Dollar	Leopard	Seal	Ox	Tiger	Whale
Salamander	Coral	Eel	Ostrich	Stingray	Frog	Jellyfish
Sole	Ferret	Ox	Lobster	Shark	Sunfish	Sea Turtle
Oyster	Sea Urchin	Oriole	Dog	Limpet	Mussel	Porpoise

_____ _____ _____   _____ _____ _____

_____ _____ _____ _____ _____   _____ _____

_____ _____   _____ _____ _____ _____ _____ _____ .

Name _____ Date _____

Plants Adapt to Their Environment

Plants and Adaptations

Plants have to adjust to the sun, rain, wind, and changing seasons. Some plants need to grow in the full sun, while others must live in the shade. Fruit trees need lots of water, but a cactus survives with very little. Plants tend to grow closer to the ground in places that are very windy. Some plants may appear dead during winter, but only the leaves or top part die off. New sprouts will appear in the spring. All of these adaptations help the plant to survive.

Match each word with its description.

1 _____ dormant

A. grow best with lots of water and full sun

2 _____ spring

B. grow best in shady areas

3 _____ ferns

C. can survive with very little water

4 _____ adaptation

D. means "sleeping" or "inactive"

5 _____ cactus

E. a tree loses it leaves to survive a cold winter

6 _____ fruit trees

F. season for new growth

Science • 3–4 © 2005 Creative Teaching Press

Name _____ Date _____

How Plants Protect Themselves

PLANTS AND ADAPTATIONS

Plants cannot run away from their enemies, so they need other ways to protect themselves from being eaten. Rosebushes, bougainvillea, and blackberry bushes have thorns. Marigolds produce an odor that insects do not like. If you touch poison ivy leaves, you will get an itchy rash. The leaves of oleander and rhubarb can make you very sick. Hemlock and nightshade are so poisonous they can cause death.

Use the words in the box to complete the sentences.

thorns	odor	poison	spines	needle-like	rash

1 The leaf edges of stinging nettle have thin, _____ projections that prick the skin and inject a stinging chemical.

2 Rosebushes have _____ on their branches.

3 Some plants contain _____ that can make you sick if you eat them.

4 Marigolds make an _____ that keeps insects away.

5 Cactus plants protect themselves with _____.

6 Touching poison ivy will give you a _____.

Name _____ Date _____

How Plants Reproduce

PLANTS AND ADAPTATIONS

Most of the plants you are familiar with produce seeds. The peach, cherry, apricot, and avocado make one large seed. Apples, tomatoes, figs, and squash make several smaller seeds. Not all plants produce seeds. Ferns and mosses reproduce by spores. Many plants can reproduce by taking cuttings from a part of the plant, or by grafting a plant part onto another plant. Other plants reproduce by sending out runners.

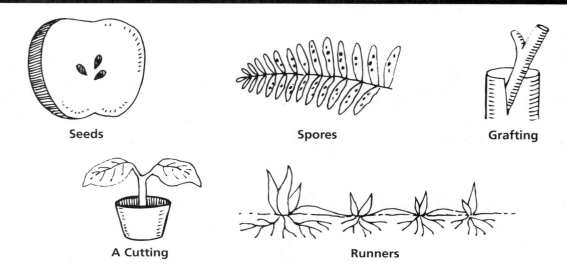

Seeds   Spores   Grafting

A Cutting   Runners

Use the words in the box to complete the sentences.

seeds	spores	cutting	grafting	runners

1 Ferns produce little packets of _____ on the underside of their leaves.

2 Flowering plants usually reproduce by making _____.

3 If you place a leaf or a piece of stem in some water and let it sprout, it

makes a _____.

4 _____ is when a budding branch of one plant is inserted into a cut made in a different plant.

5 Strawberry plants and grasses can send out _____ along the surface of the ground, which sprout roots and grow into new plants.

Seed Dispersal

PLANTS AND ADAPTATIONS

Some plants have seeds that burst out of their covering. Others have seeds that stick to our socks or an animal's fur and travel to a new place. A few seeds have little wings or hairs that let them float in the wind. Animals pick up many seeds. They may drop some of the seeds, or they may eat the fruit and the seeds will pass out with the animal's droppings. A few seeds have special coverings that allow them to float in water.

Explode

Hitchhiker

Wind

Harvester

Water

Look at the seeds. Use the pictures above to identify how each seed would travel.

Coconut

Burdock

Corn

1 _____ **2** _____ **3** _____

Maple

Milkweed

Touch-me-not

4 _____ **5** _____ **6** _____

Science • 3-4 © 2005 Creative Teaching Press

Name _____ Date _____

Unusual Plant Adaptations

PLANTS AND ADAPTATIONS

Some plants have extra roots that sprout out of their stems. These roots may help hold a plant up or attach it to a wall. Many vines are able to grow on tree trunks and branches or climb up a fence. There are several kinds of plants that live in places where the soil is low in minerals. These plants have special structures for catching insects. These plants produce chemicals to digest the insect's body and absorb its nutrients.

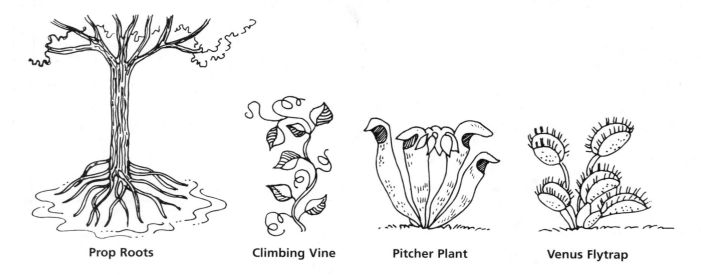

Prop Roots   **Climbing Vine**   **Pitcher Plant**   **Venus Flytrap**

Put a ✓ by the sentences that describe unusual plant adaptations.

1 _____ Most flowers come in pretty colors.

2 _____ Climbing ivy plants produce extra roots that extend out from the stems.

3 _____ Creeping fig vines produce little "tendrils" that grow out from the stem and curl around surrounding objects.

4 _____ Plants need sunshine to grow.

5 _____ The Venus flytrap catches insects to eat.

6 _____ Mangrove trees have prop roots that hold them up in the water where they grow.

7 _____ Bald cypress trees have extra roots called "knees" that stick up out of the water of a swamp.

Science • 3–4 © 2005 Creative Teaching Press

Name _____ Date _____

What's in Our Trash?

NATURAL RESOURCES

Have you ever thought about what your family throws into the trash? Or, have you ever asked where does all the trash go? Most of what we throw away ends up in a landfill. That is a special place where the city buries the trash. We are running out of room for all this trash.

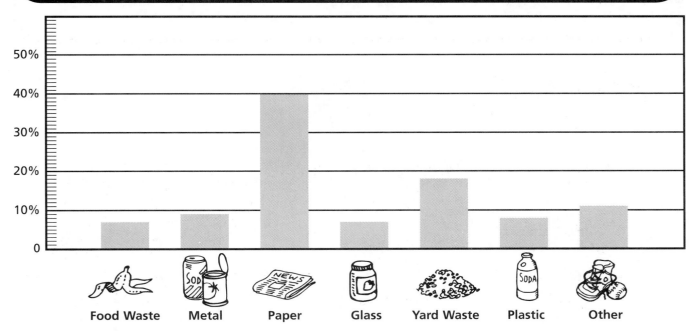

Use the graph to answer the questions.

1 The largest part of our trash is _____.

2 The second biggest part of our trash comes from _____.

3 Which do we throw away more of, metal cans or glass bottles?

_____

4 Waste such as leftover food scraps and banana peels makes up _____ % of the trash.

5 Waste such as plastic bottles from soda, milk, and dishwashing soap make up

_____ % of the trash.

6 Old shoes, clothes, and wood scraps go in the category called

_____ trash.

Name _____ Date _____

Recycling

Natural Resources

Every time we make or build something we use some of the earth's natural resources. Every time we throw something in the trash we are wasting our resources. When we try to reuse or recycle things we are saving natural resources. We can help take care of the earth by recycling paper, metal cans, and plastic bottles. We also help when we try to reuse things, or pass them on to someone else who might be able to use them.

Put a ✓ by all the items that you could recycle.

1 _____ aluminum can

2 _____ glass bottle

3 _____ T-shirt

4 _____ plastic spoon

5 _____ Styrofoam™ cup

6 _____ plastic juice bottles

7 _____ candy wrappers

8 _____ newspaper

9 _____ phone books

10 _____ plastic milk bottles

Name _____ Date _____

Fossil Fuels Give Us Energy

Natural Resources

Whenever we turn on a light, cook our food, or heat our house we are using energy. The energy usually comes from burning coal, oil, or natural gas. These things are called **fossil fuels** because they come from the remains of living things. All three fossil fuels are used to generate electricity. Natural gas is also used for cooking and heating.

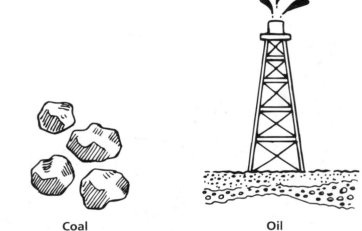

Coal   **Oil**

Natural Gas

Read each statement. Write **T** if the statement is true or **F** if it is false.

1 _____ We have to drill down into the ground to find oil.

2 _____ Natural gas and oil can be formed from the dead remains of tiny plants and animals in the ocean.

3 _____ Coal is made from the remains of plants that grew in ancient swampy areas.

4 _____ The main use for coal is generating electricity.

5 _____ Natural gas is used in many homes for cooking and heating.

6 _____ We have enough fossil fuels to last us forever.

7 _____ People today often use coal to heat their homes.

8 _____ Oil and natural gas can be used to generate electricity.

Science • 3–4 © 2005 Creative Teaching Press

Name _____   Date _____

Conservation of Our Natural Resources

NATURAL RESOURCES

Natural resources include our land, air, water, forests, and fossil fuels. The earth can recycle the air and water. We can replant forests to grow new trees. However, we cannot replace our fossil fuels so easily. Coal, oil, and natural gas take thousands of years to form. We are using them up too fast. It is important to conserve all of our natural resources.

Color in all the letters with a • and arrange the words to fit in the spaces below.

___ ___ ___ ___ ___ ___ ___   ___ ___ ___ ,   ___ ___ ___ ___ ___ ,   and   ___ ___ ___ ___ ___ ___ ___ ___ .

Name _____ Date _____

Saving Our Land and Soil

NATURAL RESOURCES

Every year farmers spray their crops with pesticides and use fertilizers. Some factories dump toxic chemicals onto the ground. Sometimes harmful substances were used in the construction of old buildings. When we tear down these old buildings, it can pollute the air and soil. We can save our land and soil with careful building and farming.

Spraying Pesticides

Using Fertilizers

Building Demolition

Put a ✔ by the things that would help to save our land and soil.

1 _____ We can grow organic crops without harmful pesticides.

2 _____ Cover all of the land with buildings to protect the soil from pollution.

3 _____ Farmers can use less pesticides and fertilizers.

4 _____ Plant bare ground so that the soil doesn't wash away in the rain.

5 _____ Plant a row of trees as a windbreak to keep the soil from blowing away.

6 _____ We can plant crops using contour farming, terracing, or strip farming.

7 _____ Support building code laws that limit the use of harmful substances in construction.

8 _____ Add more fertilizer to the soil.

Name _____ Date _____

Silicon—From Sand to Computer Chips

Natural Resources

Silicon is a very interesting natural resource found in sand. Pure silicon is shiny and silvery, but it is not a metal. The silicon is removed from the sand and made into thin, circular slices, sort of like thin cookies. Hundreds of tiny electrical circuits are layered on small pieces of the silicon. We call these pieces computer chips. The circuits can be programmed to do all sorts of things.

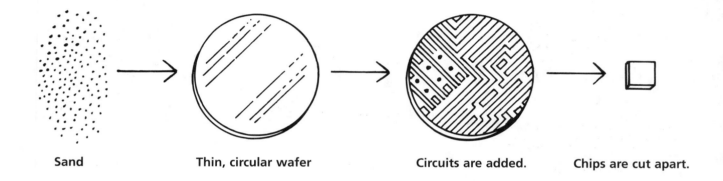

| Sand | Thin, circular wafer | Circuits are added. | Chips are cut apart. |

Put the sentences in order to show how computer chips are made from silicon.

_____ The chips are cut from the circles and inserted into a computer.

_____ Sand is dug up and brought to a factory.

_____ Pure silicon is removed from the sand.

_____ Hundreds of electrical circuits are layered on the silicon.

_____ The silicon is shaped into cylinders and cut into thin, circular slices.

Science • 3–4 © 2005 Creative Teaching Press

Name _____ Date _____

Water Cycle

NATURAL RESOURCES

The sun dries up, or evaporates, some of the water in oceans, lakes, rivers, and puddles. This invisible water, called **water vapor**, rises up into the air. The water vapor gets colder as it rises. Then condensation takes place and clouds form. When the clouds cannot hold any more moisture, we get precipitation. This process is called the **water cycle**.

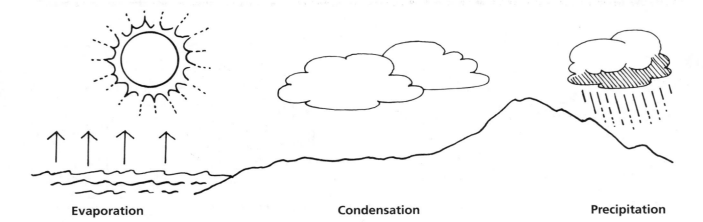

| Evaporation | Condensation | Precipitation |

Use the words in the box to complete the sentences.

| evaporation | precipitation | condensation | water vapor | clouds | sun |

1 The heat from the _____ starts the water cycle.

2 Water dries up and changes into a gas by a process called

_____.

3 Moisture falling from the sky is called _____.

4 Invisible water in the air is called _____.

5 _____ is when water vapor cools off and changes back into little drops.

6 _____ form in the sky when condensation takes place.

Name _____ Date _____

Air and Water Pollution

NATURAL RESOURCES

Many things that are released into the air or into our water cause pollution. The exhaust from our cars and smoke from factories cause air pollution. The water runoff from farms and houses can cause water pollution. Dust and dirt from building construction can add to air pollution. The propellants from spray cans can cause air pollution, too. Breathing polluted air or drinking polluted water can cause health problems.

Look at the list of things that can cause pollution. Write each term under **Water** or **Air** to show which type of pollution it causes.

| smoke | sewage spill | farm runoff | car exhaust | construction dust | litter in a river |

Water   **Air**

_____   _____

_____   _____

_____   _____

Name _____ Date _____

Structure of the Earth

GEOLOGY

The **crust** is the hard, thin, outer layer of the earth. Under the crust is the **mantle**. The mantle is mostly solid, but it becomes fluid magma under pressure. The inner part of the earth is called the **core**. It is the thickest and hottest layer. The core is divided into an outer and inner part. The inner core is very dense and contains a lot of iron and nickel.

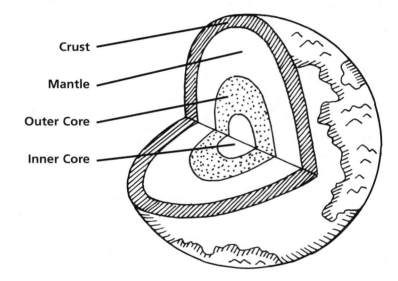

Crust
Mantle
Outer Core
Inner Core

Write **crust**, **mantle**, or **core** next to each statement to identify which part of the earth is described.

1 _____ This layer cooled off first and hardened into rock.

2 _____ We find magma in this layer.

3 _____ This is the thickest layer of the earth.

4 _____ This layer contains a lot of iron and nickel.

5 _____ The oceans cover a lot of this layer.

6 _____ Pressure builds up in this layer and pushes on the crust.

7 _____ This is the layer on which we live.

8 _____ This layer is divided into an outer and inner part.

Name _____ Date _____

Rock or Mineral?

GEOLOGY

The crust of the earth is made of rocks and minerals. A **mineral** is a naturally occurring nonliving substance. Combinations of two or more minerals make a rock. You can think of a mineral like a letter of the earth's alphabet. A rock is like an earth word. In other words, rocks are made of minerals. There are a few rocks made of just one mineral, but most rocks are made of several minerals.

Minerals

  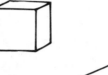 

Rocks

 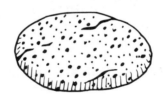 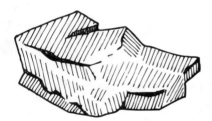

Write **M** if the sentence describes minerals or **R** if it describes rocks.

1 _____ These come in all shapes and sizes and are very common on the earth's crust.

2 _____ These form crystals with definite shapes.

3 _____ These are often used in jewelry.

4 _____ These are made of several minerals.

5 _____ These usually have just one color.

6 _____ These generally have more than one color or shade, and they can even be striped or speckled.

Science • 3–4 © 2005 Creative Teaching Press

Name _____ Date _____

Fire-Formed Rocks

GEOLOGY

Rocks that are made from the heat within the earth are called **igneous**, or **fire-formed**, **rocks**. Igneous rocks are made from the melted mineral material in the mantle, called **magma**. When magma is pushed out on top of the earth's crust, it is called **lava**. Some fire-formed rocks are made from magma that is pushed up into the crust but is trapped under the ground. Other igneous rocks are made from the lava from volcanoes.

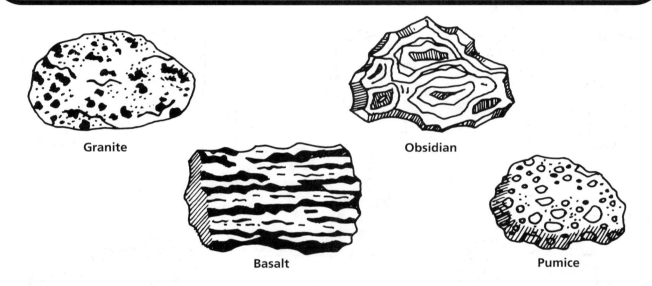

Granite

Obsidian

Basalt

Pumice

Read each statement. Write **T** if the statement is true or **F** if it is false.

1 _____ Obsidian is a shiny, black, glassy volcanic rock.

2 _____ We can see speckles in a piece of granite because it cooled and hardened quickly.

3 _____ The melted mineral material in the mantle is called lava.

4 _____ Pumice has many holes in it where bubbles of gases used to be.

5 _____ Basalt is the main igneous rock that forms the floor of the ocean.

6 _____ Granite was made from magma that was trapped in the earth's crust.

7 _____ Some pieces of pumice can float in water.

8 _____ Fire-formed rocks are called igneous rocks.

Name _____ Date _____

Volcanoes

Geology

Volcanoes can erupt, sending out steam, ash, gases, and lava. Some lava is thin and foamy and full of bubbles. Other lava is thicker and flows like toothpaste coming out of a tube. All lava cools and hardens into igneous rocks. Even the ash cools and hardens into igneous rock. A volcano can erupt many times over thousands of years. Each eruption builds up more layers of hardened igneous rock.

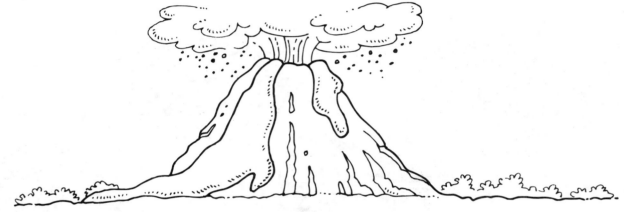

Use the words in the box to complete the sentences.

lava	gases	ash	igneous	extinct	mountain

1 A volcano forms _____ rocks.

2 Volcanoes can release _____ that smell like rotten eggs or burnt matches.

3 When a volcano has not erupted for many, many years scientists say it is

_____.

4 When hot magma comes out of a volcano we call it _____.

5 Powdery _____ can erupt from a volcano, too.

6 After many, many eruptions, the layers of a volcano can build a

_____.

Science • 3–4 © 2005 Creative Teaching Press

Name _____ Date _____

Sedimentary Rocks

GEOLOGY

Sedimentary rocks are layered rocks. They form from particles of sediment that pile up on top of each other. Layers of sand, mud, pebbles, or broken seashells build up at the bottom of the sea. After many years, the weight and pressure of all these layers harden the sediments into rock. Some sedimentary rocks are made of just one kind of sediment. Others are a combination of different kinds of particles.

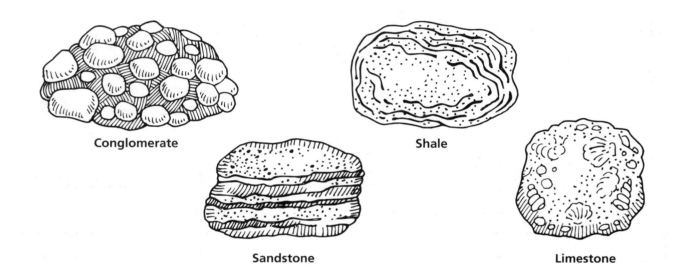

Conglomerate

Shale

Sandstone

Limestone

Read each statement. Write **T** if the statement is true or **F** if it is false.

1 _____ Sandstone is made of many layers of sand.

2 _____ Limestone is formed from mud that hardened into rock.

3 _____ Conglomerate gets its name because it is a mixture of sand and pebbles.

4 _____ The heat within the earth causes sedimentary rocks to form.

5 _____ Sandstone can be different colors.

6 _____ Some limestone has pieces of broken seashells that we can see.

7 _____ Sedimentary rocks mainly form under the ocean.

Name _____ Date _____

Caves

GEOLOGY

Caves form when rainwater dissolves limestone rock. The water seeps through cracks in the rock. The water carries the dissolved minerals with it. Gradually, a hole forms in the layers of limestone. Further in the cave, the water drips down from the ceiling. As the limestone minerals harden, **stalactites** form. The water that drips onto the floor of the cave can build up **stalagmites**.

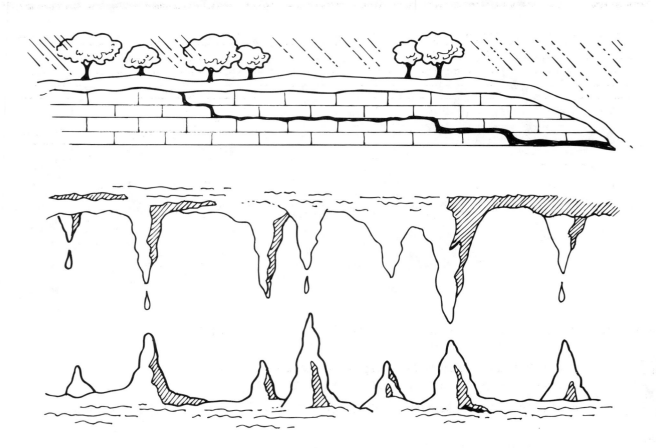

Number the sentences in order from 1–4 to show how a cave forms.

_____ Stalactites form on the ceiling and stalagmites form on the floor of the cave.

_____ Rainwater seeps through cracks in limestone rock.

_____ Water carries away the dissolved limestone minerals.

_____ A hole forms in the layers of limestone rock.

Name _____ Date _____

Metamorphic Rocks

GEOLOGY

Heat and pressure within the earth can slowly change rocks from one type into another. Sometimes magma moves into cracks within layers of sedimentary or igneous rock. The minerals in some rocks are pressed into long, thin, flat grains. The heat and pressure can cause rock layers to bend or crack. These changed rocks are called **metamorphic rocks**. Marble, slate, schist, and quartzite are common metamorphic rocks.

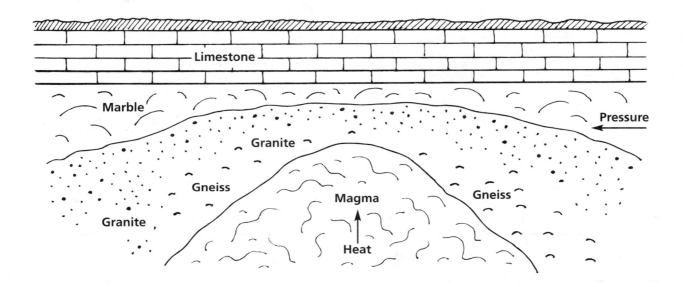

Read each statement. Write **T** if the statement is true or **F** if it is false.

1 _____ Pressure can cause rock layers to bend or crack.

2 _____ Heat can cause some rocks to melt and change into new rocks.

3 _____ Metamorphic rocks form very quickly.

4 _____ Limestone is a metamorphic rock.

5 _____ Metamorphic rocks can be changed into other types of metamorphic rocks.

6 _____ Marble is a common metamorphic rock.

7 _____ Sedimentary and igneous rocks can be changed into metamorphic rocks.

8 _____ Granite turns into a metamorphic rock called slate.

Name _____ Date _____

Rocks Are Recycled

GEOLOGY

Rocks last for a long time but not forever. As rocks break apart, they form **sediment**. This sediment can form new sedimentary rocks. The pressure created by movements of the earth's crust can cause metamorphic rocks to form. If rocks are melted into magma, new igneous rocks can form. This continuous process is called the **rock cycle**.

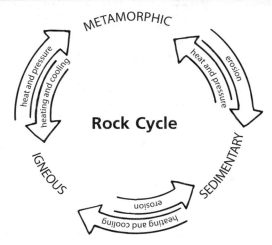

Use the words in the box to complete the sentences.

magma	pressure	sedimentary	igneous	cycle	crust

1 Movement of the earth's upper layer, or _____, helps to recycle rocks.

2 When igneous rocks wear down and break apart they can form new _____ rocks.

3 Sedimentary rocks can change into metamorphic rocks from heat or

_____.

4 Metamorphic rocks can be melted and then form new _____ rocks.

5 Heat from _____ can cause sedimentary or igneous rocks to change into metamorphic rocks.

6 The process of rocks changing into new and different rocks is called the rock

_____.

Name _____ Date _____

Ores

GEOLOGY

Ores are rocks or minerals that have a metal in them. They are mined from the earth and crushed and processed in order to obtain the metal in pure form. Then we can make many useful products from the metal. Gold and silver ore may contain veins or nuggets of the pure metal. Some ores are found close to the surface of the crust. Others are hidden deeper, and we have to build mine shafts to reach them.

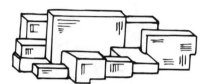

Galena (lead ore)

Bauxite (aluminum ore)

Silver ore

Match the ore with what can be made from it.

1 _____ Gold ore

2 _____ Bauxite (aluminum ore)

3 _____ Hematite (iron ore)

4 _____ Galena (lead ore)

5 _____ Chrysocolla/Malachite (copper ore)

6 _____ Scheelite (tungsten ore)

7 _____ Silver ore

A. aluminum foil, pots and pans, airplane parts

B. batteries, fishing weights, paint, solder

C. dime and quarter coins, jewelry, mirrors, film

D. pennies, gelatin molds, electrical wire, brass, jewelry

E. steel, cars, nails, screws, all kinds of machines

F. jewelry, electronic circuits, tooth "crowns"

G. wires inside light bulbs, helps make steel

Science • 3–4 © 2005 Creative Teaching Press

Name _____ Date _____

Weathering and Erosion

GEOLOGY

Weathering is the wearing away or breaking of old rocks. **Erosion** takes place when rock or soil is carried away to another place. The wind, moving water, ice, and earthquakes cause weathering and erosion. Even plant roots can slowly crack rocks. Heavy rains can cause rockslides or mudslides. Good topsoil is lost every year to erosion.

Write **W** if the sentence describes weathering or **E** if it describes erosion.

1 _____ Roots of trees and small plants growing between rocks gradually break the rocks apart.

2 _____ Moving water makes rocks on the bottom of a river have a smooth surface.

3 _____ The wind creates large sand dunes in the desert by blowing the sand from place to place.

4 _____ Floods wash away topsoil from a farm.

5 _____ Water freezes in the cracks of a rock, causing the rock to slowly break apart.

6 _____ Glaciers carry loose rocks and soil as they melt and slowly slide down a mountainside.

7 _____ An earthquake causes a crack in the side of a mountain.

8 _____ Some plant roots release chemicals that dissolve minerals in rocks.

Name _____ Date _____

Earthquakes

GEOLOGY

Any sudden movement of the earth's crust is called an **earthquake**. There are earthquakes somewhere in the world almost every day. Most of the earthquakes are too small for us to feel any movement. Scientists use a machine called a **seismograph** to record the movements of the earth's crust. An earthquake's magnitude is measured on the Richter scale. This tells us how much energy is given off by the earthquake.

Use the words in the box to complete the sentences.

faults	seismograph	Richter	shock waves	higher	destructive

1 Scientists measure the movement of the earth's crust on a machine called a

_____.

2 Earthquakes usually occur along large cracks in the earth's crust, called

_____.

3 Strong earthquakes can be very _____ to homes and buildings.

4 The _____ scale measures the magnitude of earthquakes.

5 More powerful earthquakes have a _____ magnitude.

6 Earthquakes send out _____ that travel long distances through the ground.

Uses of Rocks and Minerals

GEOLOGY

Every person in the United States uses more than 20 tons of rocks and minerals each year. How is that possible? We use rocks, sand, and gravel to make concrete and cement for road and building construction. We remove metal from minerals to make thousands of household appliances and automobiles. Mineral products are used in everything from paint to toothpaste. We even eat minerals as part of our food.

Where do we find useful rocks and minerals?

Use the words in the box to complete the sentences.

| western | toothpaste | central | construction | appliances | minerals |

1 The _____ part of the U.S. has a lot of useful rocks and minerals.

2 Many rocks are used in the _____ of buildings and homes.

3 We even eat _____ as part of our food.

4 Minerals containing metals are used to make many household

_____ .

5 The _____ part of the U.S. does not have as many useful minerals as other parts.

6 Crushed rock and minerals are used to make _____ for cleaning our teeth.

Name _____   Date _____

Geology Magic Square Puzzle

GEOLOGY

Match each word in the left column with its definition in the right column. Write the number of the word in the lettered box of the magic square. The numbers in each row across, down, and diagonally will add up to the "magic number" of 46 if your answers are correct. You will not need to use all the numbers.

1 _____ mica

2 _____ talc

3 _____ graphite

4 _____ metamorphic

5 _____ faults

6 _____ earthquake

7 _____ folding

8 _____ magma

9 _____ igneous

10 _____ crust

11 _____ core

12 _____ minerals

13 _____ diamond

14 _____ gem

15 _____ mantle

16 _____ quartz

17 _____ sedimentary

18 _____ lava

19 _____ erosion

20 _____ gypsum

A. hot molten material that comes out of a volcano

B. process when rock layers bend and wrinkle

C. rocks are made of these

D. fire-formed rocks

E. changed rocks

F. rocks made from layers of sediment

G. outer layer of the earth

H. middle layer of the earth

I. innermost layer of the earth

J. valuable rock or mineral used in jewelry

K. deep cracks in the earth's crust

L. very common mineral in the crust

M. hardest mineral on earth

N. molten material in the mantle

O. the carrying away of rock and soil from the crust

P. sudden movement of the earth's crust

A.	B.	C.	D.
E.	F.	G.	H.
I.	J.	K.	L.
M.	N.	O.	P.

Name _____ Date _____

The Ocean Floor

GEOLOGY

When you step into the ocean, you are standing on the **continental shelf**. This shelf extends out about 100 miles (161 km). Then it drops off steeply as the **continental slope**. The main floor of the ocean is called the **ocean basin**. It has landforms similar to what we see on the continents. There are mountains, valleys, and flat plains. In addition, there are deep cracks in the ocean floor called **trenches**.

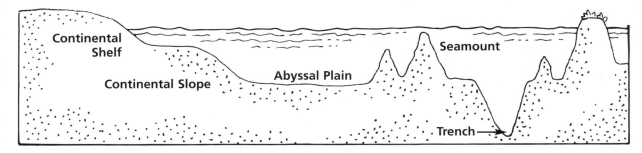

Use the words in the box to complete the sentences.

shelf	slope	plains	seamount	trench	island

1 An underwater mountain is called a _____.

2 The edge of a continent that is under the ocean is called the continental

_____.

3 A deep crack in the ocean floor is called a _____.

4 Large, flat areas on the ocean floor are called abyssal

_____.

5 The steep drop off from the continental shelf is called the continental

_____.

6 An underwater mountain that is tall enough to stick out of the water forms

an _____.

Name _____ Date _____

Fossil Records

GEOLOGY

A **fossil** can be formed from anything left behind by prehistoric life. It might be a bone, tooth, shell, or footprint impression. Casts and molds are imprint fossils. Sometimes dissolved minerals replace the remains of a plant or an animal when water seeps through the rock. Petrified wood forms this way. Scientists study the fossils in rocks to find out what the earth was like thousands of years ago.

Fossilized Bone

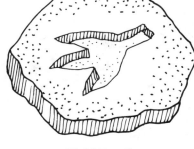

Mold Fossil

Petrified Wood

Cast Fossil

Read each statement. Write **T** if the statement is true or **F** if it is false.

1 _____ Scientists can determine the age of a fossil.

2 _____ Fossils usually form in metamorphic rock.

3 _____ We can learn about extinct plants and animals from studying fossils.

4 _____ Petrified wood is an imprint fossil.

5 _____ Many fossils of dinosaur bones have been found.

6 _____ We can find seashell fossils on the top of a mountain.

7 _____ Many seashells form cast fossils, where we see a raised impression of the shell.

Name _____ Date _____

Our Solar System

Our solar system is part of an enormous collection of stars called the **Milky Way** galaxy. The sun is at the center of the solar system. There are nine planets orbiting around the sun. Many of the planets have rings. Most of the planets have moons. The entire solar system only takes up a tiny bit of outer space.

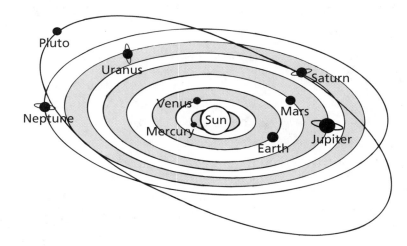

Read each statement. Write **T** if the statement is true or **F** if it is false.

① _____ All the planets travel around the sun at the same speed.

② _____ Mercury is the planet closest to the sun.

③ _____ The sun's gravity keeps the planets in orbit around it.

④ _____ There is an asteroid belt between Jupiter and Saturn.

⑤ _____ The Milky Way galaxy is just one of many, many galaxies in space.

⑥ _____ Our solar system is very small compared to all of outer space.

⑦ _____ Earth is the third planet out from the sun.

⑧ _____ Most of the planets have moons that orbit around them.

⑨ _____ Several planets have rings.

⑩ _____ The orbits of Pluto and Neptune overlap each other at times.

The Moon

ASTRONOMY

The moon is Earth's closest neighbor in space. The moon does not produce any light of its own. Instead, what we call moonlight is really sunlight that is reflected off the moon and comes to Earth. The moon has no air to breathe or water to drink. There are many mountains and craters on the moon. The moon's surface is rocky and is covered with fine dust.

Use the words in the box to complete the sentences.

craters	seas	dust	ice	light	weigh

1 The moon's gravitational pull is much less than Earth's, so on the moon you

would _____ one-sixth of your body weight on Earth.

2 Large, dark areas on the moon's surface

are called _____ because we used to think they contained water.

3 Asteroids and meteors have crashed into the moon, leaving deep dents called

_____.

4 The moon does not give off any _____ of its own.

5 Scientists have found evidence of tiny bits of _____ buried in deep craters at the poles of the moon.

6 The surface of the moon is covered with rocks and fine

_____.

Phases of the Moon

ASTRONOMY

We see the parts of the moon that reflect sunlight back to Earth. Sometimes we see the whole side of the moon lit up. This is called a **full moon**. Other times we can barely see an outline of the moon, or nothing at all. This is called the **new moon**. In between we see different shapes from a **crescent**, to a **half moon**, to a **gibbous moon**. The shape of the moon doesn't change, just the parts that we can see.

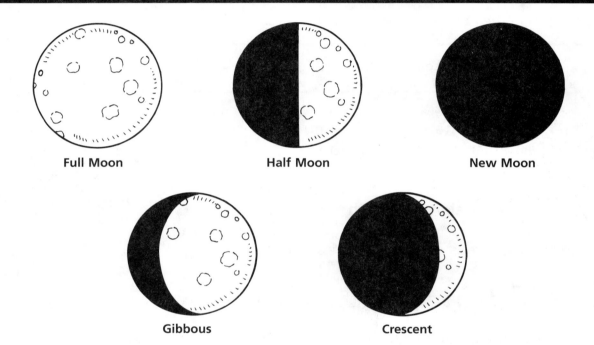

Full Moon   **Half Moon**   **New Moon**

Gibbous   **Crescent**

Read each statement. Write **T** if the statement is true or **F** if it is false.

1 _____ As the moon orbits around Earth, we can see different parts of it lit up at night.

2 _____ A crescent moon is when the moon is less than half lit up.

3 _____ The moon always reflects a lot of sunlight back to Earth.

4 _____ A gibbous moon is when the moon is more than half full but less than full.

5 _____ It takes the moon almost one month to travel all the way around Earth.

6 _____ We can hardly see anything when it is the new moon.

Science • 3–4 © 2005 Creative Teaching Press

The Sun and the Seasons

ASTRONOMY

Earth travels around the sun tilted on its axis. This tilt is what causes the seasons. Earth gets more direct rays from the sun in the summer, so it is hotter. The days are also longer in summer, so the earth heats up more. In the winter we receive the sun's rays at a slant. This spreads out the light and heat of the sun, making it colder in the winter. Days are also shorter in the winter.

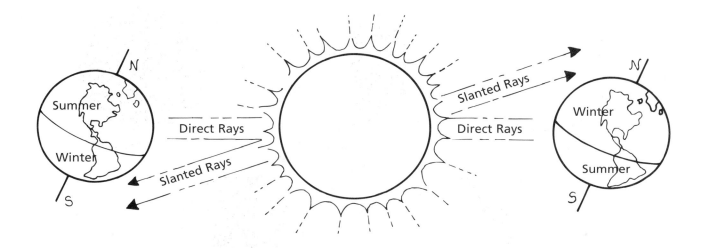

Read each statement. Write **T** if the statement is true or **F** if it is false.

1 _____ Earth is a lot closer to the sun in the summer, making it hotter.

2 _____ There are always clouds during the winter, so it is colder.

3 _____ Earth revolves around the sun tilted on its axis.

4 _____ Near the equator it always feels like summer.

5 _____ Earth is much farther away from the sun in winter, making it colder.

6 _____ Longer days in summer help to make this season warmer.

7 _____ The people in the Northern Hemisphere experience the seasons opposite of the people in the Southern Hemisphere.

8 _____ As Earth revolves, we have summer, fall, winter, and spring seasons.

Name _____ Date _____

Rotation and Revolution

Astronomy

All of the planets in our solar system move in two ways. As they travel in their orbit around the sun, they are making **revolutions**. However long it takes a planet to complete one revolution is considered a year on that planet. The other way the planets move is by turning around, or **rotating**. One complete rotation is what we call a day on that planet. All of the planets are rotating and revolving at the same time.

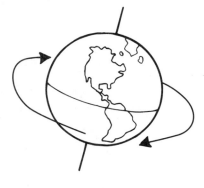
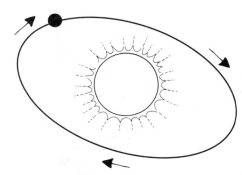

Rotation   **Revolution**

Use the words in the box to complete the sentences.

rotation	revolution	day	year	24 hours	365 days

1 When any planet travels all the way around the sun, it makes a

_____.

2 It takes Earth _____ to make one rotation.

3 It takes Earth _____ to make one revolution.

4 The time it takes for a planet to make one rotation is called a

_____ on that planet.

5 Each planet makes one revolution each _____.

6 When a planet turns all the way around on its axis, it makes a

_____.

Name _____ Date _____

The Inner Planets

ASTRONOMY

Mercury, Venus, Earth, and Mars are known as the **inner planets**. They are closer to the sun. All of the inner planets are solid and rocky and rather small in size. However, each planet is unique. Mercury has no atmosphere, while the atmosphere on Venus is made of poisonous clouds. Earth and Mars have moons, but Mercury and Venus do not. The length of their days and years is different for each planet.

Mercury   **Venus**   **Earth**   **Mars**

Write the name of the planet described in each sentence.

1 _____ This planet has a day about as long as a day on Earth.

2 _____ This planet has an atmosphere that can support life.

3 _____ This planet has a year shorter than its day.

4 _____ This is the smallest inner planet.

5 _____ Almost three-fourths of this planet is covered with oceans.

6 _____ This planet has the shortest year of the inner planets.

7 _____ This planet has an atmosphere of poisonous clouds.

8 _____ This planet has two moons.

Science • 3–4 © 2005 Creative Teaching Press

Name _____ Date _____

The Outer Planets

ASTRONOMY

Jupiter, Saturn, Uranus, Neptune, and Pluto are known as the **outer planets**. With the exception of Pluto, all of the outer planets are large and made mostly of gases. Pluto is the smallest planet and is rocky. All of the outer planets except Pluto have rings, with Saturn having the most rings. Jupiter is the largest planet and famous for its giant red spot. Uranus and Neptune are similar in size. The length of their days and years is different for each planet.

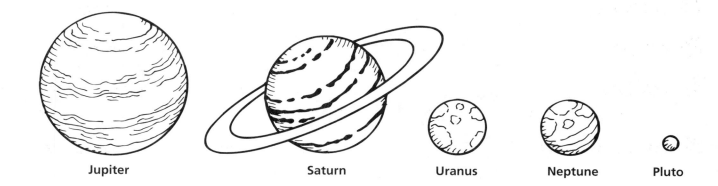

Jupiter   Saturn   Uranus   Neptune   Pluto

Write the name of the planet described in each sentence.

1 _____ This planet is the smallest planet in the solar system.

2 _____ This planet has a giant red spot, which is a whirling storm of gases.

3 _____ This planet has rings oriented in a different direction from the others.

4 _____ This planet has many bright-colored rings around it.

5 _____ This is the largest planet in the solar system.

6 _____ This faraway planet has eight moons.

7 _____ This planet only has one tiny moon.

8 _____ This planet's year would last 164 of our Earth years.

Science • 3–4 © 2005 Creative Teaching Press

Name _____ Date _____

Outer Space Word Scramble

ASTRONOMY

Unscramble the words and complete the definitions.

1 SRTAS = _____ : bright, shiny objects we see in the sky at night

2 NEPLTA = _____ : there are nine of these in our solar system

3 ONOM = _____ : an object that orbits around a planet

4 OTPLU = _____ : the smallest planet in our solar system

5 RNASTU = _____ : a large planet with many bright-colored rings

6 ONSIONCTTALLE = _____ : a group of stars that reminds us of a picture

7 ARHTE = _____ : the planet that we live on

8 UNS = _____ : the star that is closest to Earth

9 MYERRUC = _____ : the planet closest to the sun

10 SVENU = _____ : a planet close to Earth but surrounded by poisonous clouds

Name _____ Date _____

How Did the Planets Get Their Names?

ASTRONOMY

> The planets that make up our solar system were given names from Greek and Roman mythology. Each name was chosen because something about the planet reminded people of a particular god or goddess. It may be because of the way the planet looked to people long ago or the way it traveled in space.

Jupiter

Mercury

Neptune

Mars

Match the description of the god or goddess with the planet of the same name.

1 _____ Mercury

2 _____ Venus

3 _____ Earth

4 _____ Mars

5 _____ Jupiter

6 _____ Saturn

7 _____ Uranus

8 _____ Neptune

9 _____ Pluto

A. red planet next to Earth; named after the god of war

B. king-sized planet; named after the king of the gods

C. white planet close to Earth; named after the goddess of love

D. planet with fastest revolution; named after the messenger of the gods

E. planet of many colorful rings; named after the god of farming

F. faraway, blue-green planet; named after the god of the sea

G. small, dark planet; named after the god of the dark underworld

H. our planet; named after the goddess of the earth

I. faraway, bluish planet; named after the god of the sky

Science • 3–4 © 2005 Creative Teaching Press

Name _____ Date _____

Constellations

The stars in the sky are not evenly spread out. From our view on Earth we can see some stars that seem to be grouped closer together. In ancient times, people imagined they saw pictures in these star groups. We call them **constellations**. They were named after animals, heroes, gods, and goddesses. More constellations have been named in modern times. Constellations do not really exist in the sky, just in our imagination.

1.    2. 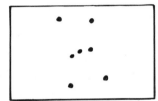   3.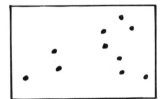

Leo, the lion   **Cassiopeia, the lady**   **Orion, the hunter in a chair**

Match the stars, shown above, with the pictures people imagined they saw.

❶ The stars for constellation #1 match with the picture of _____.

❷ The stars for constellation #2 match with the picture of _____.

❸ The stars for constellation #3 match with the picture of _____.

❹ Create your own constellation. Look at the star pattern below. Draw a picture of what you see and name it.

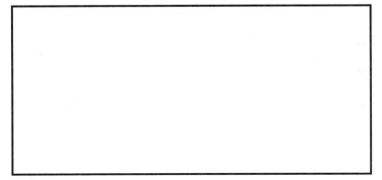

Name _____ Date _____

Why Do Stars Seem to Twinkle?

ASTRONOMY

When you gaze up at the stars on a clear night, you see many dots of shining light. These stars often seem to twinkle. The light from the stars passes through the air around Earth, called the **atmosphere**. The air around Earth is always moving. As the starlight bumps into the air, it is jiggled a little. This makes the star seem to twinkle.

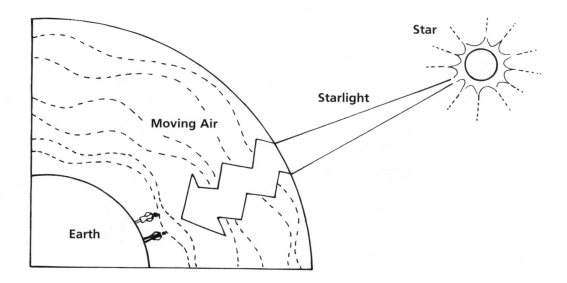

Use the words in the box to complete the sentences.

atmosphere	air	twinkle	light	space

1 The _____ around Earth is always moving.

2 The air around Earth is called the _____.

3 When we look at the stars in the sky at night, they seem to _____.

4 The _____ from the stars bumps into the air in the atmosphere.

5 If you went into outer _____, you could tell that stars do not really twinkle.

Science • 3–4 © 2005 Creative Teaching Press

Name _____ Date _____

Traveling in Space

Astronomy

It is not easy to travel in space. The hardest part is just getting there. You need a space vehicle that has strong booster rockets to overcome Earth's gravity. Then you need to bring along food, air, and water because none of these are found in outer space. If you want to go outside for a space walk, you must wear a special spacesuit to protect you. It takes hundreds of people to plan and monitor a space flight.

Read each statement. Write **T** if the statement is true or **F** if it is false.

1 _____ It is easy to travel into outer space.

2 _____ Once you are in space you are weightless.

3 _____ Astronauts eat a lot of freeze-dried food because it is lighter and takes up less room.

4 _____ Astronauts can live for long periods of time in a space station.

5 _____ Astronauts have to wear air tanks inside the space shuttle.

6 _____ Powerful rockets are used to escape Earth's gravity in order to get into space.

7 _____ Astronauts wear special spacesuits when they go outside the shuttle to do any work.

Name _____ Date _____

Static Electricity

ELECTRICITY AND MAGNETISM

Have you ever walked across the carpet in your socks and gotten a shock when you touched a doorknob? That is an example of **static electricity**. Static electricity uses no wires or batteries. It is a buildup of electrical charges **(electrons)** on an object. Static electricity results from **friction**, when one object rubs against another. Some objects lose electrons, while other materials pick up extra electrons.

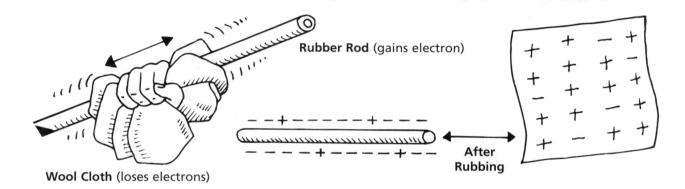

Rubber Rod (gains electron)

After Rubbing

Wool Cloth (loses electrons)

Use the words in the box to complete the sentences.

negatively	positively	electrons	rubbing	shock	neutral

1 Static electricity is caused by one material _____ against another.

2 Most of the time objects have no electrical charge and are called _____.

3 If an object loses electrons, it becomes _____ charged.

4 If an object picks up extra electrons, it becomes _____ charged.

5 If you touch an object with a different electrical charge, you will receive a _____.

6 Static electricity is caused by the transfer of _____ from one material to another.

Science • 3–4 © 2005 Creative Teaching Press

Name _____ Date _____

What Is a Battery?

ELECTRICITY AND MAGNETISM

> We use batteries every day—in flashlights, radios, many toys, and smoke alarms. What exactly is a battery? A **battery** is a little package of chemicals that can produce electricity. When it is connected in a circuit, the chemicals inside the battery begin to make electricity. There are terminals on a battery that let the electricity leave and return to the battery. Eventually, all the electricity a battery can make will be used up. Then you need a new battery.

Look at the picture. Follow the directions to mark the picture and answer the questions.

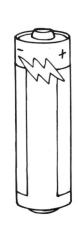

**Flashlight Battery
1.5 volts**

**Transistor Radio
Battery
9 volts**

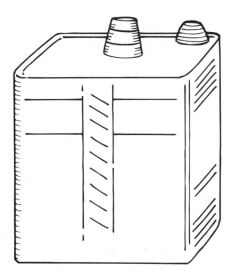

**Lantern Battery
6 volts**

1 Draw arrows to show where the terminals are on each of the batteries shown above.

2 Why don't batteries last forever? _____

_____

_____

Name _____ Date _____

What Is an Electric Circuit?

ELECTRICITY AND MAGNETISM

Electricity follows a closed path called a **circuit**. The electricity flows around and around. Circuits need something to act as the source of electricity. When you put a battery in the circuit, electricity can flow. There is usually a switch in the circuit that lets you stop the flow of electricity when needed. When the circuit is closed, electricity will flow all through the circuit. When the switch is open, you create a hole in the circuit, and the flow of electricity stops.

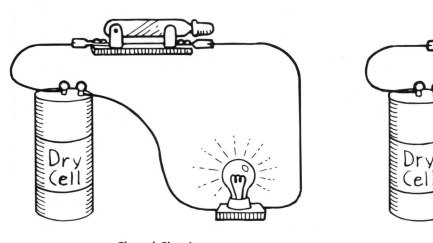

Closed Circuit

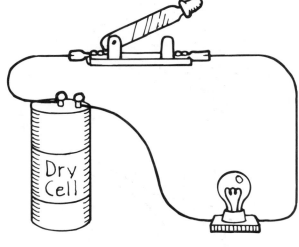

Open Circuit

Read each statement. Write **T** if the statement is true or **F** if it is false.

1 _____ In order for electricity to work, it must be able to leave a battery and return to the battery.

2 _____ The path electricity takes is called a circuit.

3 _____ Switches are used to make sure the electricity is always working.

4 _____ Batteries can supply the source of electricity in a circuit.

5 _____ Electricity does not flow in an open circuit.

6 _____ A circuit can have almost any shape as long as it is a closed circuit.

7 _____ Wires are used to connect the parts of a circuit together.

Name _____ Date _____

Conductors and Insulators

ELECTRICITY AND MAGNETISM

Conductors are materials that let electricity flow through them easily. They can be used to make wires and other things we put into an electric circuit. Some materials are better conductors than others. An **insulator** is something that does not let electricity flow through easily. We cover electrical wires with insulators. Insulators help to keep the electricity where we want it.

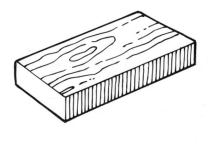  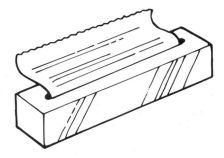

Write **conductor** or **insulator** to tell how each material acts with electricity.

1 plastic = _____

2 copper penny = _____

3 wood = _____

4 glass = _____

5 silver = _____

6 aluminum foil = _____

7 rubber eraser = _____

8 paper clip = _____

Voltage and Electric Safety

ELECTRICITY AND MAGNETISM

The push behind the electric current is called the **voltage**. It is very important to notice what the voltage is when you are working with electricity. Anything under 10 volts is safe to handle. As the voltage increases, the danger of shock and injury increases. Batteries are always marked with their voltage. The voltage wired in the walls of your home and school is around 110 volts. That is very dangerous, so be careful around electricity.

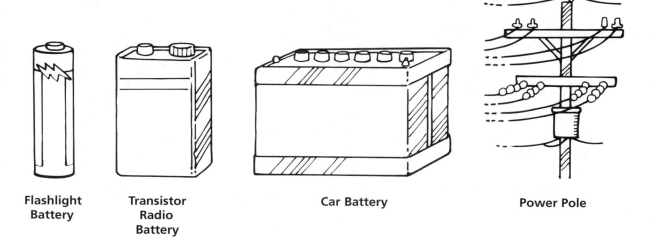

Flashlight Battery   **Transistor Radio Battery**   **Car Battery**   **Power Pole**

Read each statement. Write **T** if the statement is true or **F** if it is false.

1 _____ You should stay away from electric towers and high power lines.

2 _____ A small battery can have a higher voltage than a big battery.

3 _____ Never put any object other than a plug into an electrical outlet.

4 _____ Electricity cannot travel through your body.

5 _____ You should not overload an electrical outlet with too many plugs.

6 _____ Batteries always have their voltage stamped on them.

7 _____ Voltage is the push behind the electric current.

8 _____ Batteries can never give you a shock.

Electricity Can Produce Heat, Light, or Motion

ELECTRICITY AND MAGNETISM

Many appliances in your home use electricity to make them work. We can use electricity to produce light, heat, or motion. When the electricity is connected to some type of motor, it can make things move. Electricity makes our daily lives easier.

Write **L** if electricity is used to produce light, **H** if it is used to produce heat, or **M** if it is used to produce motion.

1. _____ sewing machine

2. _____ toaster

3. _____ iron

4. _____ blender

5. _____ flashlight

6. _____ electric fan

7. _____ lamp

8. _____ electric oven

Name _____ Date _____

Series Circuits

ELECTRICITY AND MAGNETISM

If you connect one lightbulb in a circuit, it is called a **simple circuit**. When you have more than one device connected in a single pathway, it is called a **series circuit**. The electricity leaves the battery and must travel through everything in the circuit before returning to the battery. Each device (usually lightbulbs) in the circuit uses the electricity.

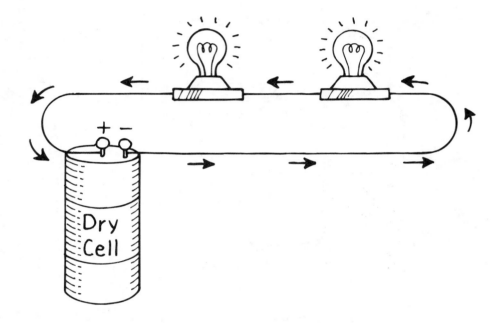

Put a ✓ by the sentences that correctly describe a series circuit.

1 _____ There is one path for the electricity to travel.

2 _____ All the lights are on, or all the lights are off.

3 _____ Each light can work independently.

4 _____ The brightness of the lights gets dimmer as you add more lights in the circuit.

5 _____ This type of circuit is commonly used in your house.

6 _____ There is more than one path for the electricity to follow.

7 _____ The brightness stays the same as you add more lights in the circuit.

Science • 3–4 © 2005 Creative Teaching Press

Name _____ Date _____

Parallel Circuits

ELECTRICITY AND MAGNETISM

There is more than one way to connect several lights in a circuit. If you have more than one pathway for the electricity to use, it is called a **parallel circuit**. Some of the electricity leaves the battery and follows one path, while other electricity can follow a different path. The electricity must still find its way back to the battery.

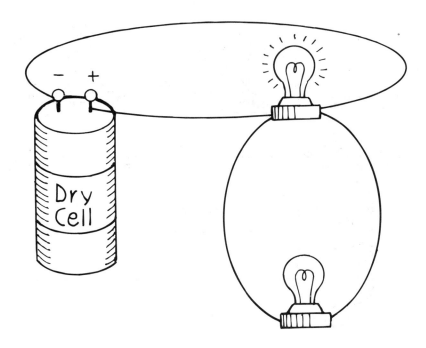

Put a ✓ by the sentences that correctly describe a parallel circuit.

1 _____ You cannot connect more than two things in the circuit.

2 _____ All the electricity follows the same path.

3 _____ There is more than one path for the electricity to follow.

4 _____ Each light will work independently.

5 _____ The brightness stays the same as you add more lights in the circuit.

6 _____ If one light burns out, all the other lights will go out, too.

7 _____ This type of circuit is commonly used in your home.

Name _____ Date _____

Batteries in Series or Parallel

ELECTRICITY AND MAGNETISM

Batteries can be wired in series, too. The negative terminal of one battery is connected to the positive terminal of the next battery. Batteries can also be wired in parallel. The negative terminal of one battery is connected to the negative terminal of the next battery, and the positive terminal of one battery is connected to the positive terminal of the next battery.

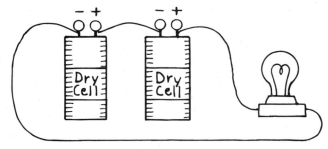

Series Connection

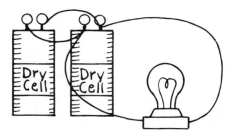

Parallel Connection

Use the words in the box to complete the sentences.

voltage	negative	three	one and a half	last longer	positive

1 If batteries are connected in series, it increases the _____.

2 The total voltage in the batteries
connected in parallel shown above will be _____.

3 The total voltage in the batteries
connected in series shown above will be _____.

4 If batteries are connected
in parallel, the batteries will _____.

5 For batteries in series, a negative terminal must be connected to a

_____ terminal.

6 For batteries in parallel, a negative terminal must be connected to a

_____ terminal.

Name _____ Date _____

Electricity Word Search

ELECTRICITY AND MAGNETISM

Find the electricity words in the word search. The words go across, down, backwards, and diagonally.

electromagnet	battery	current	motor	series
terminal	negative	static	circuit	wire
electrons	charge	voltage	energy	generator
resistance	insulator	parallel	electricity	positive

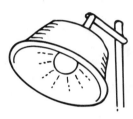

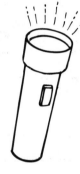

```
A R E C O O L M A R N E T I S N M B
L B A T T E R Y X N T O R B S E C W
R C D T A S T R O T A R E N E G W L
E L E C T R O M A G N E T U D A E F
T E Y N E O C M L Q U P J I R T H G
H F S D T P I C R R U K S T A I Q L
C B G V C V T B E N E R G Y T V W Z
H L A O Z D A A C L E O U S S E Y R
A O E L E C T R I C I T Y C E L A O
R V E T H O S J U O I F N G R O B T
G S P A M P S R N N H R K O I V L O
E P O G I Z T V T D V O C P W N M M
A O N E R J S E R I E S A U O Y U W
B S M L E O U R G C L Z B B I R A L
C I O C O C W N K T L C A N M T R C
U T H K R E V I T I S O P C E T O U
R I C I G N Z Z E R C T C D G O T R
R V C F T S N O R T C E L E R L A A
E E H W D B A T L O O K R A T L G
N R G L B T E R M I N A L O H A U L
T I N O T A W A X T S E N T C T S M
L X O K Z B L E L L A R A P L A N E
K P R E S I S T A N C E R I C B I T
```

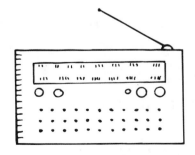

Science • 3–4 © 2005 Creative Teaching Press

Name _____ Date _____

What Is a Short Circuit?

ELECTRICITY AND MAGNETISM

A **short circuit** occurs when electricity finds a path that is easier to travel than the one we intended. It is harder for electricity to flow through a lightbulb than to go through a wire. Short circuits are dangerous because electricity is flowing through the circuit even though we do not see any lights on. The wires in a short circuit can get very hot and start a fire in your house. Or, short circuits can use up all the electricity in a battery in a short time.

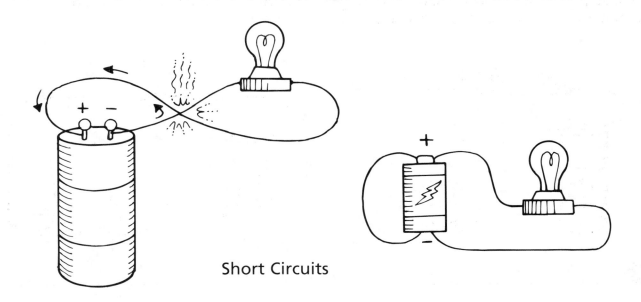

Short Circuits

Put a ✓ by the things that could cause a short circuit.

1 _____ Old electrical cords that have their insulating covering worn away

2 _____ Connecting three lights in a series circuit

3 _____ Continuously walking over an electrical cord under an area rug

4 _____ An open circuit built with batteries, lights, and wires

5 _____ Connecting a wire from the negative terminal to the positive terminal of the same battery

6 _____ Removing plugs from a wall outlet by pulling on the cord instead of the plug

Name _____ Date _____

What Type of Circuit Is It?

ELECTRICITY AND MAGNETISM

A **closed circuit** lets electricity flow through it and back to the battery. An **open circuit** has a hole in it and the electricity cannot return to the battery. A **simple circuit** just has one device (usually a light) connected to the battery. Or, a circuit could be connected in series or in parallel. A **short circuit** allows the electricity to take a shortcut to get back to the battery.

Look at the circuit pictures. Under each picture, write **open** or **closed** on the first line. On the second line, tell if it is a **simple**, **series**, **parallel**, or **short** circuit.

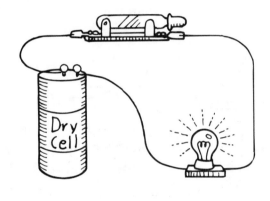

1 _____

_____

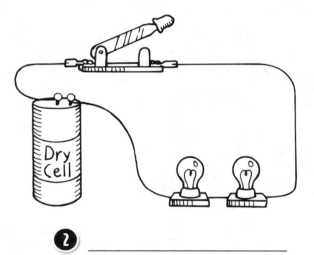

2 _____

_____

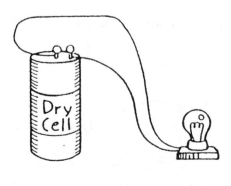

3 _____

_____

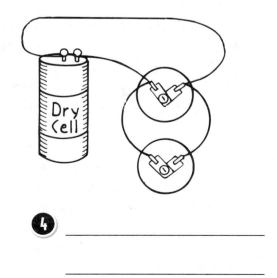

4 _____

_____

Name _____ Date _____

Electrical Resistance

ELECTRICITY AND MAGNETISM

Resistance determines how easy or hard it is for an electric current to flow through something. All wires do not have the same resistance. Resistance depends on the length and thickness of the wire, as well as what the wire is made of. When there is more resistance in a circuit, the wires get hot.

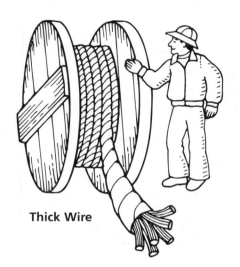

Thick Wire

Thin Wire

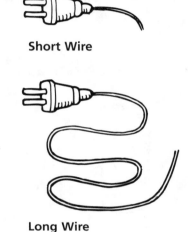

Short Wire

Long Wire

The type of wire determines the amount of resistance in the circuit.

Choose the object that would produce more resistance. Write your choice on the line.

1 _____ A thick wire or a thin wire

2 _____ A long wire or a short wire

3 _____ A wire connecting a radio or a wire inside an iron

4 _____ A wire inside a lightbulb or a wire inside a tape player

5 _____ A wire connecting a fan or a wire inside a toaster

6 _____ A wire made of copper or a wire made of nichrome (nickel and chrome)

Name _____ Date _____

An Electric Meter

ELECTRICITY AND MAGNETISM

Power plants generate electricity and send it to our schools and homes over wires. An **electric meter** is a device that measures the amount of electricity we use. The meter reading helps determine our electric bill. Someone from the utility company reads the meter and records the numbers each month. If an arrow on the meter is between two numbers, they record the lower number. The zero counts as a zero next to the one, but it counts as ten when it comes after the nine.

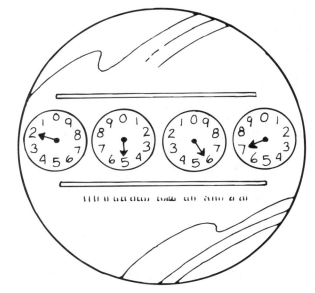

The numbers are read and recorded from left to right.

Look at the pictures and answer the questions.

1 What is the reading on the meter pictured above? _____

2 If the meter read 4945 one month, and it read 6690 the next month, how many units of electricity (called kilowatt-hours) did your family use during that time? _____ kilowatt-hours

3 If the arrow on a meter dial is between the 4 and 5, what number would be recorded? _____

4 If the arrow on a meter dial is between the 0 and the 1, what number would be recorded? _____

5 If the arrow on a meter is between the 9 and 0, what number would be recorded? _____

Name _____ Date _____

Magnetic Attraction

ELECTRICITY AND MAGNETISM

The invisible energy that allows a magnet to pick up things made of iron or steel is called **magnetic attraction**. This energy is felt in the space around the magnet, which is called the **magnetic field**. The energy always goes from one end of a magnet to the other. The ends of a magnet are called the **poles**. When two magnets are placed near each other, the magnetic field can either pull them together or push them apart.

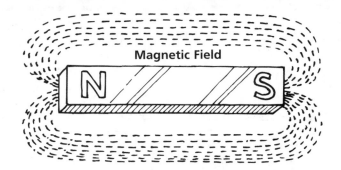

Magnetic Field

Magnetic Field

Use the words in the box to complete the sentences.

attract	repel	magnetic field	poles	iron	shape

1 The space around a magnet where its energy is felt is called the

_____.

2 The ends of a magnet are called the _____.

3 Magnets are able to pick up things made of steel or _____.

4 If two like poles are placed next to each other, the magnets will

_____ each other.

5 If two unlike poles are placed next to each other, the magnets will

_____ each other.

6 The shape of a magnetic field depends upon the _____ of the magnet.

Name _____ Date _____

How Does a Compass Work?

ELECTRICITY AND MAGNETISM

The needle of a compass is a small magnet. We can use a compass to find our direction because the earth itself is like a giant magnet. The center of the earth contains a lot of iron. And the earth is surrounded by its own magnetic field. The compass needle points towards the North Pole of the earth.

Use the words in the box to complete the sentences.

west	east	south	north	magnet	direction

1 The needle of a compass is a _____.

2 A compass can help us find our _____.

3 The compass Manuel is holding would tell him that the library is to the

_____ of him.

4 The pond is to the _____ of where Manuel is standing.

5 The cat is to the _____ of where Manuel is standing.

6 The sun will be setting to the _____ of where Manuel is standing.

Name _____ Date _____

Magnetism and Electricity

ELECTRICITY AND MAGNETISM

You can make a magnet using electricity. This type of magnet is called an **electromagnet**. It is made of a coil of wire wrapped around something made of iron or steel. When electricity flows through the coil of wire, a magnetic field is created around the wire. This makes the piece of iron turn into a magnet.

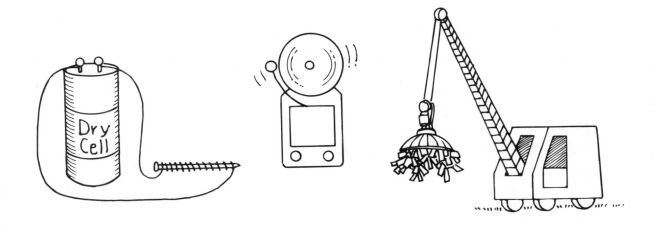

Read each statement. Write **T** if the statement is true or **F** if it is false.

1 _____ You can make an electromagnet weaker by increasing the number of coils of wire.

2 _____ An electromagnet is only a magnet when the electric current is flowing.

3 _____ A bell rings because there is an electromagnet inside.

4 _____ Electromagnets are used in junkyards to pick up scrap metal and move it to another place.

5 _____ You must use a wire made of iron to create an electromagnet.

6 _____ When electricity flows through a wire, a magnetic field is created around the wire.

Name _____ Date _____

Generators

ELECTRICITY AND MAGNETISM

A **generator** is a device that produces electricity. It is made of a magnet and a coil of wire. The coil of wire spins inside the magnetic field of the magnet. Or, the magnet can spin inside a big coil of wire. Power plants have gigantic generators in them. They produce the electricity that is sent to our homes and schools.

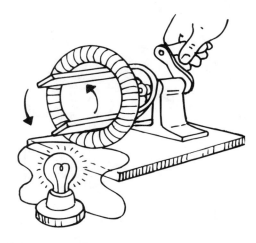 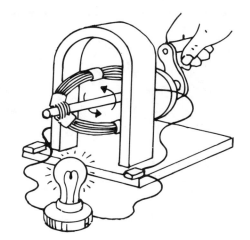

Use the words in the box to complete the sentences.

energy	generators	steam	magnet	coil	electricity

1 Power plants have very large _____ that produce electricity.

2 We have to pay for the _____ used to make the generators work.

3 A generator is made of a _____ and a

_____ of wire.

4 If you turn a coil of wire within a magnetic field, you will create

_____ .

5 Generators can work using the energy from _____,
burning coal, oil, or natural gas.

Science • 3–4 © 2005 Creative Teaching Press

Name _____ Date _____

Electric Motors

ELECTRICITY AND MAGNETISM

Motors are used to make things move. A motor contains a spinning electromagnet and a permanent magnet. There is a part inside the motor that reverses the direction of the electric current. This changes the poles of the electromagnet. As a result, the electromagnet spins as it is attracted to and then repelled by the permanent magnet. We can connect all kinds of machines to a motor to use this spinning energy.

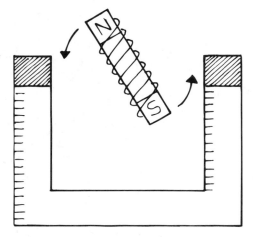
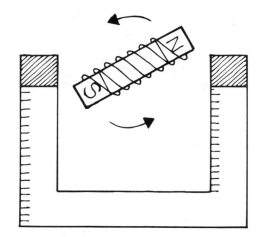

The reversing poles make a motor spin.

Put a ✓ by the things that contain an electric motor that makes them work.

1 _____ A radio

2 _____ An electric fan

3 _____ A sewing machine

4 _____ A vacuum cleaner

5 _____ A mop

6 _____ A flashlight

7 _____ A washing machine

8 _____ A train

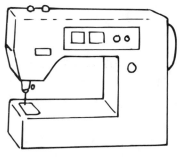

Science • 3–4 © 2005 Creative Teaching Press

Name _____ Date _____

Light

LIGHT ENERGY

Light is a form of energy that our eyes can see. Light travels forward in a straight line but in a wave motion. The waves move up and down, sort of like a roller coaster. These energy waves travel very fast, at a speed of 186,000 miles (299,300 km) per second. Our main source of light is the sun.

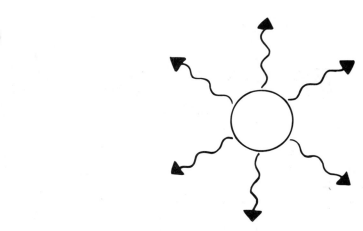

Bright Light   **Dim Light**   **Light travels in a straight line.**

Use the words in the box to complete the sentences.

bright	dim	color	wave	sun	straight

1 Light energy travels in a _____ motion.

2 Most of our light comes from the _____.

3 Light travels from its source to a destination in a _____ line.

4 Our eyes see taller light waves as _____ light.

5 Our eyes see shorter light waves as _____ light.

6 The bumpiness of a light wave, called its frequency, determines the

_____ of the light.

Name _____ Date _____

What Is Visible Light?

LIGHT ENERGY

We cannot see every type of light energy wave. We can only see the colors of the rainbow (red, orange, yellow, green, blue, indigo, and violet). These colors are known as the **visible spectrum**. A red light wave has a lower frequency. The bumpiest light wave we can see is violet light.

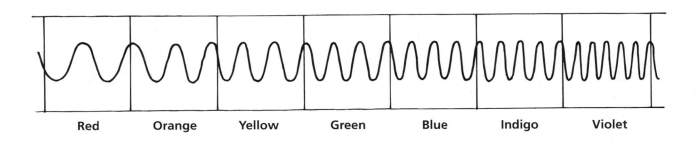

Red   **Orange**   **Yellow**   **Green**   **Blue**   **Indigo**   **Violet**

Read each statement. Write **T** if the statement is true or **F** if it is false.

1 _____ Green light has a higher frequency than red light.

2 _____ Visible light is made up of six colors.

3 _____ We cannot see infrared light, but we feel it as heat.

4 _____ Usually, all the colors of light are mixed together as white light.

5 _____ The height, or amplitude, of a light wave determines the color we see.

6 _____ Humans cannot see ultraviolet light, but many insects can.

7 _____ Our eyes interpret light waves with different frequency ranges as different colors.

8 _____ Visible light is part of a larger electromagnetic spectrum, which contains other energy waves.

Name _____ Date _____

Light and Objects

LIGHT ENERGY

When light waves strike an object, three things can happen. The light may travel through the object. The light may bounce off the object and be reflected. Or, the light waves may be blocked by the object and not allowed to pass through. This blocked light is mainly absorbed by the object and turned into heat. A shadow is formed where the light is blocked.

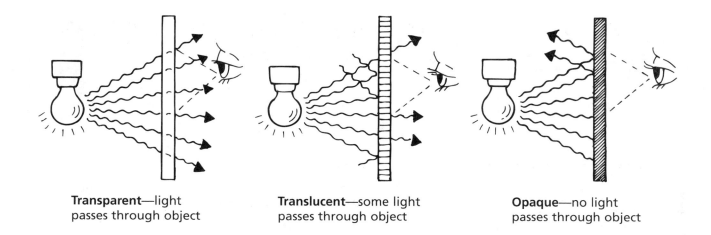

Transparent—light
passes through object

Translucent—some light
passes through object

Opaque—no light
passes through object

Read each statement. Write **T** if the statement is true or **F** if it is false.

1 _____ You can see clearly through transparent objects.

2 _____ Opaque objects form shadows.

3 _____ Transparent objects can have a color.

4 _____ Translucent objects let you see clearly through them.

5 _____ Many shower curtains, wax paper, and tissue paper are translucent.

6 _____ A person is a translucent object.

7 _____ Transparent objects absorb most of the light that strikes them.

8 _____ Cardboard, aluminum foil, and wood are opaque objects.

Name _____ Date _____

Reflection of Light

Light Energy

When light waves bounce off an object, we say they are reflected. Almost every object reflects some of the light that strikes it. Some objects reflect light better than others. Mirrors are good reflectors because they make the light bounce back to our eyes. Then we can see ourselves in the mirror.

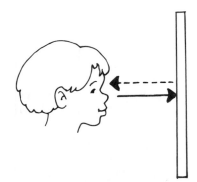
Mirror

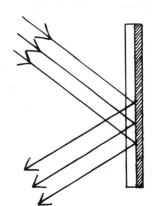
Smooth Surface

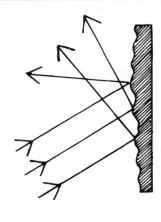
Rough Surface

Use the words and phrases in the box to complete the sentences.

in back of it	reflected	smooth	rough	polish	at an angle

1 To see a good reflection, the surface of an object must be _____.

2 If light strikes an object at an angle, it will bounce off _____.

3 When you stand in front of a mirror, you appear to be _____.

4 Objects with a _____ surface scatter the light in different directions.

5 Kaleidoscopes and periscopes work because light inside of them is

_____.

6 We clean and _____ furniture so that it will give a better reflection.

Science • 3–4 © 2005 Creative Teaching Press

Name _____ Date _____

How We See Colors

LIGHT ENERGY

Sunlight, or white light, is made of all the colors of the rainbow mixed together. When light strikes an object, some of the light is absorbed and some of the light is reflected to our eyes. We see the color that is reflected. If an object reflects all the colors, it is seen as white. If the object does not reflect any colors, we see it as black. Objects that light up or glow produce their own light, which can be white or colored.

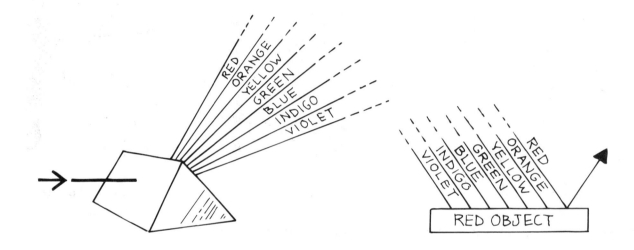

Match each object with its description.

1 _____ A white object

2 _____ A black object

3 _____ A green object

4 _____ A firefly or a glowworm

5 _____ Sunlight

6 _____ Absorb more light and change it into heat

7 _____ Reflect more light and feel cooler

A. made of all the colors of the rainbow

B. animals that produce their own light

C. light-colored clothes

D. reflects all the colors of light

E. absorbs all the colors of light

F. reflects only green lights

G. dark-colored clothes

Name _____ Date _____

Bending of Light Waves

Light Energy

Light waves travel in a straight line. However, we can make light change directions. It changes directions when it is reflected. Light can also be made to bend and change directions when it passes from one material to another. The bending of light is called **refraction**. Light is bent when it passes from air into water, or when it passes through a glass prism or lens.

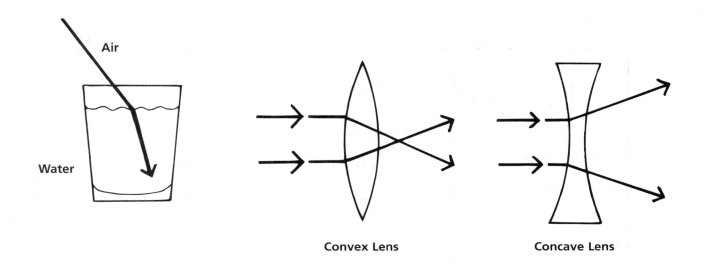

Convex Lens   Concave Lens

Put a ✓ by the things that would cause the light to be bent, or refracted.

1 _____ Light passes through the air.

2 _____ Light passes through the water of a swimming pool.

3 _____ Light passes through a magnifying glass.

4 _____ Light strikes a mirror.

5 _____ Light passes through a prism.

6 _____ Light passes through someone's eyeglasses.

7 _____ Light passes through a camera to take a picture.

Light Maze Puzzle

LIGHT ENERGY

Start at the top and find your way out of the maze. As you correctly move through the maze, you will come across letters that spell out a message. Write the letters you come across on the lines below to spell out the message.

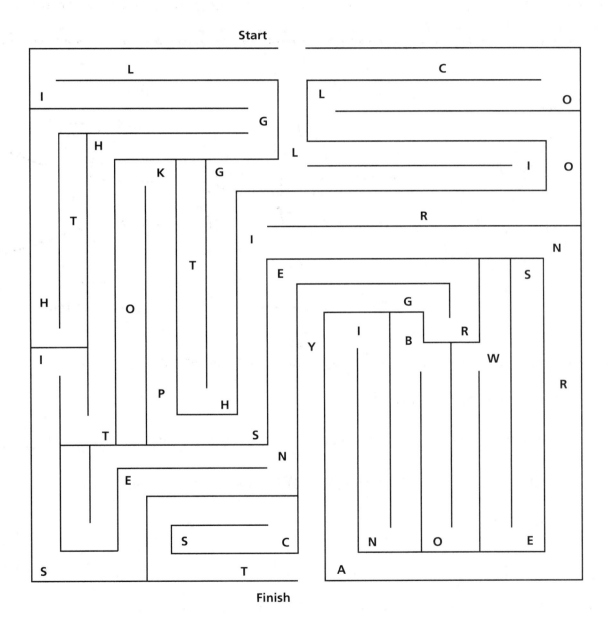

___ ___ ___ ___ ___ ___   ___ ___ ___   ___ ___ ___ ___ ___ ___ ___ ___ ___.

Name _____ Date _____

Sources of Heat

HEAT ENERGY

Our main source of heat is the sun. Heat is also produced by electricity. Did you know a lightbulb actually gives off more heat energy than light? Burning fuels like wood, coal, natural gas, or oil also produce heat. You can even produce heat from rubbing your hands together.

Sources of Heat

What is the source of heat? Write **sun**, **electricity**, or **burning fuel** to identify it.

1 _____ An iron gets hot to remove wrinkles from clothes.

2 _____ The ocean water at the beach warms up.

3 _____ A campfire can keep us warm.

4 _____ An electric blanket makes the bed warm in winter.

5 _____ We can use natural gas to cook our food.

6 _____ Snow melts from the roof of a house.

7 _____ Warm winds blow across the desert.

Science • 3–4 © 2005 Creative Teaching Press

Name _____ Date _____

How Heat Travels

Heat Energy

Heat travels in three ways. It moves through solids by **conduction**, as moving molecules bump into one another and pass the heat along. Heat moves through gases and liquids by **convection**. This is when currents of air or water move up and down. Heat can even travel through outer space by **radiation**. Heat can radiate, or spread out, from a hot object, too.

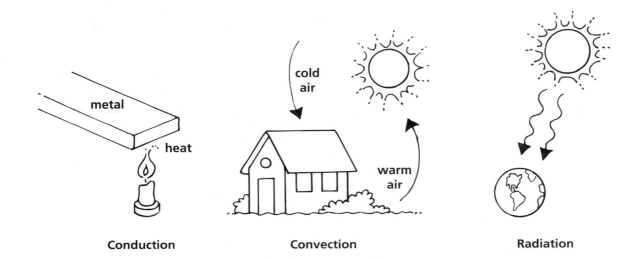

Conduction   Convection   Radiation

How does the heat travel? Write **conduction**, **convection**, or **radiation** to identify it.

1 _____ Cold air sinks towards the ground.

2 _____ Heat travels through a frying pan when we're cooking our food.

3 _____ We open windows on a hot day to cool off our house.

4 _____ The sun's rays travel through outer space to reach the earth.

5 _____ Our hands get warm when we hold a mug of hot chocolate.

6 _____ We can see smoke rising from a chimney.

7 _____ Boiling water starts to bubble up in a pot.

Name _____ Date _____

Friction Causes Heat

HEAT ENERGY

> **Friction** is another word for rubbing. When one object rubs against another, they both get warmer. That is because one material resists moving across the other. Hard, smooth surfaces produce less friction than soft or sticky surfaces. Friction sometimes helps things to work properly. Other times friction is harmful.

Read each statement. Write **helpful** or **harmful** to describe the effect of friction.

1 _____ The brakes on a car rub against the inside of the wheel to make the car stop.

2 _____ We rub a match across the side of a matchbox to light it.

3 _____ Friction makes the parts inside a motor get hot.

4 _____ The toe on an ice skate has jagged edges that catch in the ice.

5 _____ A car's broken tailpipe makes sparks as it drags along the street.

6 _____ Factories have to replace machine parts that get worn out due to friction.

7 _____ We use sandpaper to smooth the surface of a piece of wood.

8 _____ The soles of our shoes get worn away by walking a lot.

Name _____ Date _____

Measuring Heat

Heat Energy

Almost everything around you is made of tiny pieces called **molecules**. Molecules are always moving. Heat energy makes them move faster. We measure the effect of this heat energy with a thermometer. A **thermometer** tells us the temperature of something. Two types of thermometers commonly used are the Fahrenheit and Celsius.

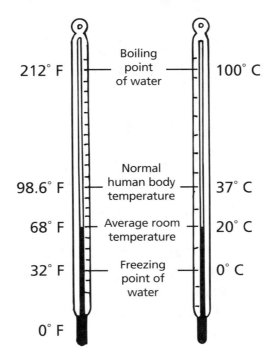

Use the numbers and words in the box to complete the sentences.

32	0	212	100	98.6	Celsius	Fahrenheit

1 Water freezes at _____°F or at _____°C.

2 Most scientists use _____ thermometers.

3 A _____ thermometer is commonly used in the United States for everyday purposes.

4 Water boils at _____°F or at _____°C.

5 Normal body temperature on a Fahrenheit thermometer is _____°F.

Name _____ Date _____

States of Matter

CHEMISTRY

Nearly everything you can see or touch is made of matter. **Matter** is anything that takes up space and weighs something. All of this matter exists in three forms or states: **solid**, **liquid**, or **gas**. Molecules in a solid are very close together. The molecules in a liquid are touching, but they can slip and slide past each other. The molecules in a gas spread far apart.

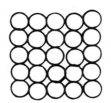 Molecule vibrates in place

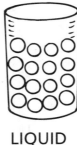 Molecules can move about

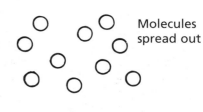 Molecules spread out

SOLID   **LIQUID**   **GAS**

Write **solid**, **liquid**, or **gas** to identify which type of matter is described in each sentence.

1 _____ This matter has no definite shape or size.

2 _____ This matter keeps its shape because its molecules are very close together.

3 _____ The molecules in this matter can be poured from one container to another.

4 _____ This matter has a definite size, or amount, but it has no shape of its own.

5 _____ This state of matter will spread out to fill up whatever container it is in.

6 _____ A rock, a nail, and a marble are examples of this state of matter.

7 _____ Milk and orange juice are examples of this state of matter.

8 _____ The air is a mixture of this state of matter.

Name _____ Date _____

Changes of State

CHEMISTRY

Matter can change from one state to another by changing the temperature. When you heat solids, they melt and become liquids. Liquids can evaporate and turn into a gas. Liquids can freeze and change into a solid. Gases can cool and condense back into a liquid.

Melting

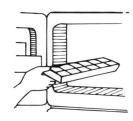
Evaporation

Freezing

Condensation

Write **freezing, melting, evaporation,** or **condensation** to identify how matter changes its state in each sentence.

1 _____ Water is removed from wet clothes by a clothes dryer.

2 _____ An ice-cream cone starts to drip on a warm day.

3 _____ Water turns to ice in a freezer.

4 _____ Little drops of dew form on the grass in the early morning.

5 _____ Rain puddles dry up after the sun comes out.

6 _____ An ice-cold glass of water starts to "sweat" on the outside of the glass.

7 _____ Brown sugar turns into a liquid when heated.

8 _____ Snow forms inside clouds when the temperature is very cold.

Name _____ Date _____

Physical Changes

Chemistry

You can break matter into smaller pieces. You can change the shape of the matter, or change its state. You can even dissolve the matter in some water. In all of these changes, you still have the same kind of matter you started with. If no new matter is created, it is called a **physical change**.

Physical Changes

Put a ✓ by the examples that are physical changes in matter.

1 _____ Paper is cut into small pieces.

2 _____ Water is boiled.

3 _____ A nail rusts.

4 _____ Clay is shaped into a bowl.

5 _____ Food is cooked.

6 _____ Aluminum foil is wrapped around an apple.

7 _____ A candle is burned.

8 _____ Salt is dissolved in some water.

Name _____ Date _____

Atoms and Molecules

CHEMISTRY

All matter is made of very tiny particles that are too small to see with our eyes. **Atoms** are the smallest pieces of matter that still have all the characteristics of that matter. An atom of gold is the smallest piece of gold. **Molecules** are combinations of two or more atoms. Water is made of molecules. Water molecules contain oxygen and hydrogen atoms.

Hydrogen Atom

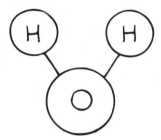

Water Molecule

Read each statement. Write **T** if the statement is true or **F** if it is false.

1 _____ Atoms make up all matter.

2 _____ There are many kinds of molecules.

3 _____ Molecules are made of several atoms.

4 _____ Atoms are larger than molecules.

5 _____ Most matter exists as single atoms.

6 _____ Atoms and molecules are too small to see with our eyes.

7 _____ An atom is the smallest piece of matter that has all the properties of that matter.

8 _____ There are a little over 100 different kinds of atoms.

Name _____   Date _____

Mixing and Creating New Matter

Chemistry

We can mix different kinds of matter together. Often, no new matter is created. It is just mixed together. However, sometimes we put different kinds of matter together and new matter is formed. A chemical reaction must take place to create new matter.

Fruit salad is a mixture.

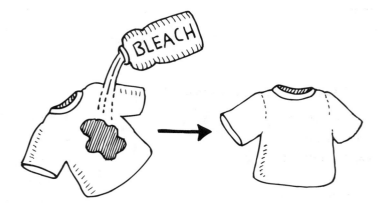

Bleach creates new matter as it removes a stain.

Put a ✔ by the mixtures that do **NOT** create new kinds of matter.

1 _____ Mixing raisins, nuts, and granola to make trail mix

2 _____ Adding sugar to water and lemon juice to make lemonade

3 _____ Stirring sawdust and sand together

4 _____ Baking a mixture of cake mix, water, oil, and eggs to make a cake

5 _____ Mixing vinegar and oil together to make salad dressing

6 _____ Mixing dry cereal and milk in a bowl

7 _____ Mixing lemon juice with buttermilk to make soft cheese curds and whey

Answer Key

What Is a Biome? (page 5)

1. tundra
2. grassland
3. rain forest
4. desert
5. forest
6. grassland
7. rain forest
8. desert

What Is a Food Chain? (page 6)

1. Color the plants green.
2. Circle the rabbit.
3. Draw an X on the fox.
4. soil

Food Chain Crossword Puzzle (page 7)

Across

1. producer
4. air
8. earth
9. omnivore
10. herbivore

Down

1. prey
2. consumer
3. sun
5. environment
6. carnivore
7. decomposer

Food Webs (page 8)

1. Draw a line from the sun to the corn plants and the grass.
2. Possible answers include any 3 of these: chickens, cows, sheep, or the farmer.
3. Put a ✓ by the corn, grass, farmer, sheep, cows, and chickens.
4. farmer
5. Circle the sheep.

Deserts (page 9)

1. saguaro cactus
2. jackrabbit
3. roadrunner
4. coyote
5. prickly pear cactus
6. kangaroo rat

Tropical Rain Forests (page 10)

1. T
2. F
3. T
4. T
5. T
6. T
7. T
8. T
9. F
10. T

Evergreen Forests (page 11)

1. b
2. b
3. c
4. a
5. a
6. a
7. d

Hardwood Forests (page 12)

1. F
2. T
3. T
4. T
5. F
6. T
7. T
8. T
9. T
10. F

Grasslands and Prairies (page 13)

1. warm
2. giraffes, lions
3. food
4. cows, horses
5. kangaroo
6. Africa
7. grassland

Arctic Tundra (page 14)

The following should have a ✓: 1, 4, 5, 6, 9, and 10.

Life in a Marsh (page 15)

1. pollution
2. wetland
3. floods
4. birds
5. recreation
6. food
7. destroyed
8. grasses

Life in a Swamp (page 16)

1. B
2. A
3. D
4. C
5. F
6. E

Life in a Bog (page 17)

1. moss
2. colder
3. water
4. cranberries
5. rosemary
6. ecosystem

Animal Migration (page 18)

Gray whale order is 4, 1, 3, 2.

Pacific salmon order is 1, 3, 4, 2, 5.

How Animals Protect Themselves (page 19)

1. quills
2. bad smell
3. bright colors
4. bark
5. roar
6. claws
7. fangs and a hiss
8. horns
9. tentacles
10. sharp teeth

Bird Beaks and Feet (page 20)

Bird feet
1. walking
2. scratching
3. swimming
4. perching

Bird beaks
1. fishing
2. eating insects
3. sucking nectar
4. straining water

How Animals Find and Catch Food (page 21)

1. tentacles
2. claws
3. sticky tongue
4. smell
5. sharp teeth
6. echolocation
7. web

Animals Adapt to Their Environment (page 22)

1. C
2. G
3. F
4. W
5. F
6. C
7. H
8. G
9. C
10. H

How Animals Reproduce (page 23)

1. eggs
2. eggs
3. born alive
4. eggs
5. born alive
6. eggs
7. eggs
8. eggs

Circle frog, insects, most fish, worms.
Draw a box around chicken, dog, human beings, alligator.

Spider or Insect? (page 24)

Spiders
1. Legs: 8 (all attached to abdomen)
2. Eyes: usually have 8 simple eyes
3. Body parts: 2 (head and abdomen)

Insects
1. Legs: 6 (all attached to thorax)
2. Eyes: 2 compound eyes and a few simple eyes
3. Body parts: 3 (head, thorax, and abdomen)
4–5. Answers will vary. Possible answers include:
    Spiders usually live on land.
    Spiders have no antennae.
    Spiders do not have wings.

Most spiders spin silk (from spinnerets on their abdomen).

Spiders are usually carnivorous (paralyzing prey with poison).

Insects are found on land and in water.

Insects have antennae.

Insects usually have wings

Most insects do not spin silk, but if they do it is from glands in their mouth.

Insects eat plants, animals, and even decayed material.

Butterfly or Moth? (page 25)

Color 1 and 6 orange (butterflies).

Color 3 and 4 brown (moths).

Draw an X on 2 and 5.

What Animal Are You Like? (page 26)

1. Swan
2. Ox
3. Bee
4. Fox
5. Bat
6. Owl
7. Peacock
8. Goose

Animals of Long Ago (page 27)

1. F
2. F
3. T
4. F
5. T
6. T
7. T
8. T

Tide Pools (page 28)

1. sea snails, barnacles, limpets, mussels
2. sea urchin, sea anemone, starfish, crab
3. Answers will vary. Possible answer: The seaweed plants just flop over on the rocks (they can't move to a new place) and wait for the tide to come back in.

Sandy Beaches (page 29)

The following should have a ✓: 2, 4, 5, 7, 8, and 10.

The Ocean's Sunlight Zone (page 30)

1. G
2. I
3. H
4. C
5. A
6. E
7. D
8. F
9. B

The Ocean's Twilight and Midnight Zones (page 31)

1. T
2. F
3. T
4. F
5. T
6. T
7. T
8. F

Life on a Coral Reef (page 32)

1. fan
2. staghorn
3. skinny
4. fat
5. starfish, sea urchin

Sea Turtles (page 33)

The following should have a ✓: 2, 3, 4, 5, 7, 8, and 9.

Marine Mammals (page 34)

1. blubber
2. sea otter
3. teeth
4. walrus
5. sea lion
6. baleen

Types of Fish (page 35)

1. D
2. B
3. C
4. B
5. C
6. C
7. B
8. D

Plankton (page 36)

1. plankton
2. microscope
3. plant
4. drift
5. food
6. animal

Seashell Animals (page 37)

1. T
2. F
3. T
4. F
5. F
6. T
7. T

Seabirds (page 38)

1. swim
2. dive
3. albatross
4. seagull
5. wade
6. pelican

Sea Life Puzzle (page 39)

The following should be crossed out:
tuna, seagull, crab, marlin, shrimp, plankton, salmon, halibut, dolphin, sand dollar, seal, whale, coral, eel, stingray, jellyfish, sole, lobster, shark, sunfish, sea turtle, oyster, sea urchin, limpet, mussel, and porpoise.

Message: The sea gives us lots of food.

Plants Adapt to Their Environment (page 40)

1. D
2. F
3. B
4. E
5. C
6. A

How Plants Protect Themselves (page 41)

1. needle-like
2. thorns
3. poison
4. odor
5. spines
6. rash

How Plants Reproduce (page 42)

1. spores
2. seeds
3. cutting
4. grafting
5. runners

Seed Dispersal (page 43)

1. water
2. hitchhiker
3. harvester
4. wind
5. wind
6. explode

Unusual Plant Adaptations (page 44)

The following should have a ✓: 2, 3, 5, 6, and 7.

What's in Our Trash? (page 45)

1. paper
2. yard waste
3. metal cans
4. 7
5. 8
6. other

Recycling (page 46)

The following should have a ✓: 1, 2, 6, 8, 9, and 10.

Fossil Fuels Give Us Energy (page 47)

1. T
2. T
3. T
4. T
5. T
6. F
7. F
8. T

Conservation of Our Natural Resources (page 48)

Reduce use, reuse, and recycle.

Saving Our Land and Soil (page 49)

The following should have a ✓: 1, 3, 4, 5, 6, and 7.

Silicon—From Sand to Computer Chips (page 50)

The order should be 5, 1, 2, 4, 3.

Water Cycle (page 51)

1. sun
2. evaporation
3. precipitation
4. water vapor
5. condensation
6. clouds

Air and Water Pollution (page 52)

Water pollution: sewage spill, farm runoff, litter in a river

Air pollution: smoke, car exhaust, construction dust

Structure of the Earth (page 53)

1. crust
2. mantle
3. core
4. core
5. crust
6. mantle
7. crust
8. core

Rock or Mineral? (page 54)

1. R
2. M
3. M
4. R
5. M
6. R

Fire-Formed Rocks (page 55)

1. T
2. F
3. F
4. T
5. T
6. T
7. T
8. T

Volcanoes (page 56)

1. igneous
2. gases
3. extinct
4. lava
5. ash
6. mountain

Sedimentary Rocks (page 57)

1. T
2. F
3. T
4. F
5. T
6. T
7. T

Caves (page 58)

The order should be 4, 1, 2, 3.

Metamorphic Rocks (page 59)

1. T
2. T
3. F
4. F
5. T
6. T
7. T
8. F

Rocks Are Recycled (page 60)

1. crust
2. sedimentary
3. pressure
4. igneous
5. magma
6. cycle

Ores (page 61)

1. F
2. A
3. E
4. B
5. D
6. G
7. C

Weathering and Erosion (page 62)

1. W
2. W
3. E
4. E
5. W
6. E
7. W
8. W

Earthquakes (page 63)

1. seismograph
2. faults
3. destructive
4. Richter
5. higher
6. shock waves

Uses of Rocks and Minerals (page 64)

1. western
2. construction
3. minerals
4. appliances
5. central
6. toothpaste

Geology Magic Square Puzzle (page 65)

A. 18	B. 7	C. 12	D. 9
E. 4	F. 17	G. 10	H. 15
I. 11	J. 14	K. 5	L. 16
M. 13	N. 8	O. 19	P. 6

The Ocean Floor (page 66)

1. seamount
2. shelf
3. trench
4. plains
5. slope
6. island

Fossil Records (page 67)

1. T
2. F
3. T
4. F
5. T
6. T
7. T

Our Solar System (page 68)

1. F
2. T
3. T
4. F
5. T
6. T
7. T
8. T
9. T
10. T

The Moon (page 69)

1. weigh
2. seas
3. craters
4. light
5. ice
6. dust

Phases of the Moon (page 70)

1. T
2. T
3. F
4. T
5. T
6. T

The Sun and the Seasons (page 71)

1. F
2. F
3. T
4. T
5. F
6. T
7. T
8. T

Rotation and Revolution (page 72)

1. revolution
2. 24 hours
3. 365 days
4. day
5. year
6. rotation

The Inner Planets (page 73)

1. Mars
2. Earth
3. Venus
4. Mercury
5. Earth
6. Mercury
7. Venus
8. Mars

The Outer Planets (page 74)

1. Pluto
2. Jupiter
3. Uranus
4. Saturn
5. Jupiter
6. Neptune
7. Pluto
8. Neptune

Outer Space Word Scramble (page 75)

1. stars
2. planet
3. moon
4. Pluto
5. Saturn
6. constellation
7. Earth
8. sun
9. Mercury
10. Venus

How Did the Planets Get Their Names? (page 76)

1. D
2. C
3. H
4. A
5. B
6. E
7. I
8. F
9. G

Constellations (page 77)

1. Cassiopeia
2. Orion
3. Leo
4. Answers will vary.

Why Do Stars Seem to Twinkle? (page 78)

1. air
2. atmosphere
3. twinkle
4. light
5. space

Traveling in Space (page 79)

1. F
2. T
3. T
4. T
5. F
6. T
7. T

Static Electricity (page 80)

1. rubbing
2. neutral
3. positively
4. negatively
5. shock
6. electrons

What Is a Battery? (page 81)

1. The 1.5-volt flashlight battery has terminals on the top and bottom.
   The 9-volt transistor radio battery has both terminals on the top.
   The 6-volt lantern battery has two coils of wire on top that are the terminals.
2. Batteries do not last forever because the electricity the battery produces gets used up (e.g., in a radio, toy).

What Is an Electric Circuit? (page 82)

1. T
2. T
3. F
4. T
5. T
6. T
7. T

Conductors and Insulators (page 83)

1. insulator
2. conductor
3. insulator
4. insulator
5. conductor
6. conductor
7. insulator
8. conductor

Voltage and Electric Safety (page 84)

1. T
2. T
3. T
4. F
5. T
6. T
7. T
8. F

Electricity Can Produce Heat, Light, or Motion (page 85)

1. M
2. H
3. H
4. M
5. L
6. M
7. L
8. H

Series Circuits (page 86)

The following should have a ✓: 1, 2, and 4.

Parallel Circuits (page 87)

The following should have a ✓: 3, 4, 5, and 7.

Batteries in Series or Parallel (page 88)

1. voltage
2. one and a half
3. three
4. last longer
5. positive
6. negative

Electricity Word Search (page 89)

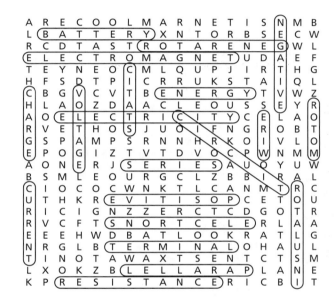

What Is a Short Circuit? (page 90)

The following should have a ✓: 1, 3, 5, and 6.

What Type of Circuit Is It? (page 91)

1. closed, simple
2. open, series
3. closed, short
4. closed, parallel

Electrical Resistance (page 92)

1. thin wire
2. short wire
3. inside an iron
4. inside a lightbulb
5. inside a toaster
6. nichrome

An Electric Meter (page 93)

1. 2567
2. 1745
3. 4
4. 0
5. 9

Magnetic Attraction (page 94)

1. magnetic field
2. poles
3. iron
4. repel
5. attract
6. shape

How Does a Compass Work? (page 95)

1. magnet
2. direction
3. north
4. east
5. west
6. west

Magnetism and Electricity (page 96)

1. F
2. T
3. T
4. T
5. F
6. T

Generators (page 97)

1. generators
2. energy
3. magnet, coil
4. electricity
5. steam

Electric Motors (page 98)

The following should have a ✓: 2, 3, 4, 7, and 8.

Light (page 99)

1. wave
2. sun
3. straight
4. bright
5. dim
6. color

What Is Visible Light? (page 100)

1. T
2. F
3. T
4. T
5. F
6. T
7. T
8. T

Light and Objects (page 101)

1. T
2. T
3. T
4. F
5. T
6. F
7. F
8. T

Reflection of Light (page 102)

1. smooth
2. at an angle
3. in back of it
4. rough
5. reflected
6. polish

How We See Colors (page 103)

1. D
2. E
3. F
4. B
5. A
6. G
7. C

Bending of Light Waves (page 104)

The following should have a ✓: 2, 3, 5, 6, and 7.

Light Maze Puzzle (page 105)

Light is energy.

Sources of Heat (page 106)

1. electricity
2. sun
3. burning fuel
4. electricity
5. burning fuel
6. sun
7. sun

How Heat Travels (page 107)

1. convection
2. conduction
3. convection
4. radiation
5. conduction
6. convection
7. convection

Friction Causes Heat (page 108)

1. helpful
2. helpful
3. harmful
4. helpful
5. harmful
6. harmful
7. helpful
8. harmful

Measuring Heat (page 109)

1. 32, 0
2. Celsius
3. Fahrenheit
4. 212, 100
5. 98.6

States of Matter (page 110)

1. gas
2. solid
3. liquid
4. liquid
5. gas
6. solid
7. liquid
8. gas

Changes of State (page 111)

1. evaporation
2. melting
3. freezing
4. condensation
5. evaporation
6. condensation
7. melting
8. freezing

Physical Changes (page 112)

The following should have a ✓: 1, 2, 4, 6, and 8.

Atoms and Molecules (page 113)

1. T
2. T
3. T
4. F
5. F
6. T
7. T
8. T

Mixing and Creating New Matter (page 114)

The following should have a ✓: 1, 2, 3, 5, and 6.